# BALLET DESIGNS AND ILLUSTRATIONS 1581-1940

*Frontispiece*. BERNARDO BUONTALENTI. Design for costumes, probably in the Florentine *Intermezzi* of 1589.
Coloured drawing.

Victoria and Albert Museum

# BALLET DESIGNS
# AND ILLUSTRATIONS
# 1581-1940

*A Catalogue Raisonné by BRIAN READE*

London: Her Majesty's Stationery Office: 1967

Printed in England for Her Majesty's Stationery Office
Text by The Curwen Press, Plaistow, London, E.13
Monochrome plates by Clarke & Sherwell Ltd.
Colour plates by Jarrold & Sons Ltd., Norwich

# Foreword

IT has long been a policy of the Museum to acquire prints and drawings relating to the European theatre, and a large proportion of this special collection of designs for scenery and costumes is connected directly or indirectly with the ballet. Associated with this main group of theatrical prints and drawings in the Museum is the original material connected with the ballet in the Museum Library; also that in the Gabrielle Enthoven Collection, an integral collection, contained in the Department of Prints and Drawings, but confined to records of the London stage from the early eighteenth century onwards. The present *catalogue raisonné*, undertaken by Mr. Brian Reade, Deputy Keeper of Prints and Drawings, offers an introduction to the visual aspects of the history of the ballet by way of commentaries on the plates; and these represent a fair selection from the sources mentioned above.

In the British Isles the constantly increasing popularity of the ballet gained recognition some years ago in the establishment of The Royal Ballet as a national institution. It seems appropriate therefore, that a choice of what constitutes in fact the national collection of ballet designs and illustrations should be published by the Museum to bring it to the notice of a larger public, and to provide an informative survey for students of ballet history.

TRENCHARD COX

# Introduction

THE designs and illustrations reproduced in this book are all in the Victoria and Albert Museum, and they can be seen either in the Library, or in the Enthoven Theatre Collection, or in the Print Room of the Department of Prints and Drawings.

Most of the material is divisible into two classes: designs for costumes and designs for scenery, including designs for projects which never materialised. To these may be added contemporary illustrations of a pictorial character, and portraits of dancers in action that are valuable as records of the appearance of costumes for which the original designs in some cases no longer exist.

Though some of the seventeenth-century drawings of costumes and scenery may have been commemorative, few working designs at any period were carried out with other than a utilitarian purpose. They were intended to be guides to the wardrobe workshops where the clothes were cut and sewn, and to the craftsmen who painted the actual scenery. The designs may have been beautifully or badly drawn, but in either case they were means to ends—to ends in which the pencil of the designer played no direct part.

Most drawings, including designers' sketches, have both human and artistic interest apart from the interest attaching to any ulterior motives there might have been in making them. But since the chief aim of the ballet designer is to invent elevations and decorations, his work will be judged best in association with the plans of the choreographer, the librettist and the composer, when that is possible. The finished ballet, which is judged by the public who pays for it, is an interpretation of these plans and elevations as a building is the interpretation of an architect's calculations and conceptions. Unlike a building, however, a ballet's interpretation varies in quality according to the merits of the dancers, the musicians, the stage technicians and the audiences.

This is not an occasion for adding to the many histories of the ballet that have been written in recent times. Although the Museum collections do indeed illustrate the outline of European ballet history from the sixteenth to the twentieth centuries, neither they nor any other collections could be said to do so evenly. Nor are the Museum collections so large or so specialised as those, for example, in the *Bibliothèque Nationale* or the *Bibliothèque de l'Opéra*. On the other hand, while it seems unlikely that a representative array of works of art showing the chief stages in the evolution of the ballet will find a home in one place together, nobody in future engaged on the history of the subject can very well ignore the existence of some of the things reproduced in the following pages.

Mention must be made therefore at this point of the best features, and also of the limitations, of the Museum collections.

First in historical, if not aesthetic value, there are the drawings by Buontalenti (Plates 3–5). These date back to the very earliest years of the ballet in its embryonic form of the intermezzo; and if there is anything, except in Florence and the Louvre, comparable with these, it has yet to be made known. A somewhat larger group of drawings for a similar sort of entertainment in France in the early part of Louis XIII's reign is contained in a book bound in a vellum case which came to England some time after the French Revolution (Plates 8–14). The designs in this book are all for costumes, and they are all coloured, but are not so well executed as the Buontalenti drawings. Their interest for the historian, however, is nearly as great, and they are certainly in the rare class. To roughly the same period belongs the design by Alfonso Parigi for an inferno scene in the once famous opera *Le Nozze degli Dei* (Plate 18). Although this is a design for operatic scenery, it happens to be equally a design for balletic scenery, made at a time when operas incorporated ballets of a fantastic nature. As a drawing it is of course unique; and it is of further interest in that it differs considerably from the etching of the same subject by Stefano Della Bella made probably several years afterward in 1637.

Both the Library and the Department of Prints and Drawings contain prints relating to the seventeenth-century ballet, and to other entertainments of the period, such as the horse ballet and the carrousel, each of which had affinities with the old tournaments and pageants of the Middle Ages, without being in reality either a tournament or a pageant but a reinterpretation of a semi-choreographic form known to the Greeks and Romans. None of these seventeenth-century prints is so uncommon as to be found only in the Victoria and Albert Museum, with the possible exception of the one by Worm (Plate 39), which does not seem to have been published before. But there is nothing, except in Paris, to equal the large volume containing forty-six drawings of costumes and dances of the *ballet de cour* from which a selection has been made for Plates 22 and 24–35. If the best of these are indeed by Henry Gissey, as is believed, then in truth they ought never to have left France, and we should rejoice in their presence in our national collections if only because the pre-Berain phase of design they represent would otherwise be a great deal more obscure to us. Designs by Berain himself are rare, but the drawing reproduced in Plate 45 is tentatively attributed to him and there are two authentic productions of his studio (Plates 41, 44).

For the eighteenth century there is far less to show than for the previous century. Among the more interesting French designs of this period are two in the style of J. B. Martin attributable to an artist called Lior (Plates 57 and 58); and another in the style of Louis René Boquet (Plate 62), which may be for an opera costume purely and simply, or for a costume in the type of opera that included *ballet-divertissements*. All three drawings are probably fair copies of originals for use in the wardrobe workshops of the time.

By the early eighteenth century the ballet had gained a footing in England, but there is no contemporary document of this event in any of the Museum Departments. The next drawing of special interest is a sketch attributed to Paul Sandby showing two male dancers, intended presumably to represent Gaëtan and Auguste Vestris in action during their first visit to London in 1780–1781 (Plate 68). Though this drawing counts as a record of costumes, it is different in kind from all the ones referred to above, being primarily a satire in the English taste. From the end of the eighteenth century comes a print in the series known as *Lady Hamilton's Attitudes*, not often seen in such a context (Plate 72). Her mimes were private exhibitions, but they seem to have had an influence on certain of the Neo-Classic productions, which may have been underestimated.

Most aspects of the Romantic ballet in the next century are represented in the Museum by prints, including the celebrated lithographs after Chalon showing Marie Taglioni, Carlotta Grisi and others. Less well-known than these, and of more intellectual interest possibly, are the drawings by Chalon from a group of caricatures of leading theatrical personages of the 1820s and 1830s (Plates 102–104). A useful source of records for the scenery of the later Romantic ballet is *The Illustrated London News* in its earlier numbers, though it must be admitted that the general style of this scenery is similar to that of the operas and dramas of the middle nineteenth century. An interesting exception is the scenery for *Electra, or The Lost Pleiad* (Plate 120), which harks back, unintentionally perhaps, to the complex kind of stage mechanism fashionable in the seventeenth century.

Some lithographs of ballet costumes from Eduard Bloch's *Album der Bühnen Costüme* of 1859 are reproduced in Plates 121–124, not on account of their artistic merit, since three are little more than re-statements of contemporary photographs, but because their value as illustrations seems to have been ignored. One of these (Plate 124) has a special significance in that it introduces a Russian ballerina, Nadejda Bogdanova, somewhat early in the sequence of illustrations.

By the end of the nineteenth century the English had evolved the popular ballet of the pantomime. The sense of the word pantomime here is entirely insular, because the English stage productions known under that name were, and still are, fairy ballad-operas incorporating burlesque diversions, as well as *ballet-divertissements*. For the Victorian and Edwardian pantomimes which appeared at the Alhambra, Drury Lane, and at many of the big provincial theatres of the period, artists like Comelli and Wilhelm (alias William Pitcher), to mention the best remembered, made excellent costume designs (Plates 125–128, 130). The Museum is fortunate in possessing a lot of this material for which there is no exact equivalent on the continent.

In the selection shown in Plates 131–137, 140–146, 150–164, the Diaghilev Ballet is fairly, though not widely, represented. Picasso's contribution, for instance, cannot be represented at all. The costume designs by Bakst are well-known, and among his best, but were made late in his life for *The Sleeping Princess* in an eighteenth-century manner not really typical (Plates 153–156). The drawing by Benois for Nijinsky's clothes as the Slave of Armide (Plate 131) and Roerich's design for the camp in *Polovtsian Dances from Prince Igor* (Plate 132) are of course landmarks in the history of the twentieth-century ballet; and the stage designs by Larionov for *Les Contes Russes* (Plates 145, 146) and Gontcharova's backcloth for the London revival of *The Firebird* in 1926 (Plate 164) are among the most interesting drawings to survive from their association with Diaghilev. In 1961 an opportunity occurred for the Museum to acquire from these two artists a selection from the best of the ballet designs still belonging to them in Paris, and thus the second phase of the Diaghilev Ballet, to the character of which both Gontcharova and Larionov contributed so much, is now well represented by designs for such famous ballets as *Le Coq d'Or*, *Le Soleil de Nuit*, *Kikimora*, *Renard* and *Les Noces* (Plates 133–137, 140, 142, 143, 157–159).

From time to time the Museum has acquired drawings by artists for productions of the English school of pure ballet which grew up in the second quarter of the present century, but not enough of them yet to justify extending the selection of this book to cover that development. Apart from a group of late designs by Gontcharova for the 1940 production of *La Foire de Sorotchinsky* therefore (Plates 171–173), the selection stops in the 1930s, with a drawing by Stern for costumes in an ice ballet, just to remind the reader that popular ballet of the pantomime type has since flourished more in the variety theatre (Plate 170).

Nothing has been included that is not a work of art in the familiar sense, with the two exceptions perhaps of Della Bella's plans of an equestrian ballet (Plate 23) and an etched page from a choreographic score (Plate 47), which are little more than works of conventional craftsmanship. All the plates have been made from contemporary records: reproductions of drawings that are really translations into other media such as engraving or lithography, and therefore works of art in a modest way, have been included, but not facsimiles and mechanical or photographic reproductions.

Anyone wishing to pursue the history of the European ballet with the aid of the notes in this book might consult the works mentioned in the short bibliography included. The publications listed in the bibliography are represented either in the Museum Library or in the Library of the Enthoven Collection in the Department of Prints and Drawings.

PATIN, Jacques (worked second half of the sixteenth century).

I  FIGURE DE LA SALLE. Illustration showing the *Ballet Comique de la Reine* in progress in the Grande Salle de Bourbon of the Louvre on Sunday, 15th October, 1581. From leaf 4 (recto) in the volume *Le Balet Comique de la Royne* by Baltazar de Beaujoyeulx, published in Paris in 1582.

*Etching;* $8\frac{1}{2} \times 5\frac{3}{4}$.                                      Library

*The* Ballet Comique de la Reine, *of which the beginning is portrayed here on too small a scale, was the invention of Baldassarino da Belgiojoso, otherwise Baltazar de Beaujoyeulx, who was commissioned to devise this entertainment as part of the celebrations in honour of the marriage of Anne, Duc de Joyeuse and Marguerite de Lorraine-Vaudémont, younger sister of Queen Louise of France. Beaujoyeulx's book records the libretto and music and describes the action of the piece, and was published in the following year with plates by Jacques Patin,* peintre du roi, *who had been responsible for designing the clothes and scenery. The verse by the Sieur de la Chesnaye, King's almoner, and the music by the Sieur Lambert des Beaulieu, assisted by Maître Salmon, were conceived under the supervision of Beaujoyeulx, to whom can be credited the form and production of the ballet.*

*Dramatic entertainments had been frequent at the French court since the later Middle Ages, though among all these fêtes, mummeries and masquerades referred to briefly in memoirs and chronicles from the fourteenth to the sixteenth centuries not all included dancing. Beaujoyeulx, or Belgiojoso, had come to France as a violinist in the retinue of the Maréchal de Brissac, and in 1567 he entered the service of Catherine de Médicis. His book* Le Balet Comique de la Royne *was however the first literary, musical and visual record in France of a performance of this nature, which not only included dancing, but was conceived as a ballet. It was performed in the Grande Salle de Bourbon in the Louvre before Henri III and Catherine de Médicis, the Queen Mother (whose backs are seen at the front in the print, with Catherine on the right), and consisted of verse recitations, singing and dancing, designed to represent a pseudo-mythical theme of the kind that had been in vogue in Italian courts since the revival of Classical studies. The people taking part in this ballet were members of the court, and the form of the French* ballet de cour, *thus found, survived with many changes almost to the end of the* ancien régime, *with a period of intense popularity under Louis XIII and the youthful Louis XIV. Here we see it in its primitive stage, with various scenic properties, such as the bocage on the right with Pan sitting in it, and, on the opposite side, the gilded cave surrounded by clouds and containing singers to echo the songs sung by the main performers, all awaiting their turn to be the centre of attention when the action of the piece required this. At the end of the hall was a trellised garden where Circe presided, and either side of it were passages for the entrances and exits of performers and allegorical cars etc.*

*The dances were performed at intervals by a group of naiades which included the Queen Louise; and the naiades seem to have expressed their dramatic roles in true balletic fashion, not as irrelevant* divertissements. *Choreographic details of the dancing however were not recorded, and the costumes of those who actually danced were not illustrated in the book. The ballet concluded with a ball in which many of the rest of the court took part.*

*Beaujoyeulx's production owed its* réclame *in its period to the belief that in it he had successfully revived the classical drama with its declamations, singing and dances. The word* comique *signified not that the performance was burlesque but that it ended happily.*

PATIN, Jacques (worked second half of sixteenth century).

**2** The Four Virtues in the *Ballet Comique de la Reine*, 1581. From leaf 40 (verso) in the volume *Le Balet Comique de la Royne* by Baltazar de Beaujoyeulx, published in Paris in 1582 (see also Plate 1).

*Etching; cut to* $5\frac{1}{2} \times 8\frac{3}{16}$                                                                                   Library

*The entry of the Four Virtues made the third* intermède, intermedio *or* intermezzo *of the* Ballet Comique de la Reine. *The first Virtue carried a pillar symbolising Courage, the second a balance for Justice, the third a cup for Temperance and the fourth a serpent for Prudence. Two of them (says Beaujoyeulx in the account of 1582) sang verses to the accompaniment of lutes played by the other two, though Patin shows only one carrying a lute, and how she managed to carry the pillar as well is not explained.*

*The costumes of the Virtues were sky-blue decorated with golden stars, and their headdresses were of silk and gold. Apart from the forms of the headdresses, these costumes differ scarcely from the court clothes of the time.*

*Italian and French ballets of this period included many features with neither dancing nor miming, and it was from vocal and choral intermezzi that the Italian opera was evolved during the later years of the sixteenth century.*

BUONTALENTI, Bernardo, called Buontalenti delle Girandole (1536–1608).

**3, 4** Designs (2) from a group of four for stage scenery in the *Intermezzi* presented at Florence in the festivities held in 1589, in honour of the marriage of the Grand Duke Ferdinand I of Tuscany with Christina of Lorraine.

*Pen, ink wash and water-colour*

**3** INTERMEZZO II. The contest of the Muses and the Pierides (*La Gara fra Muse e Pieridi*).
  The hill of Parnassus is surmounted by the figure of Pegasus, below which are a number of mythological personages, and on the stage level a chorus of nymphs.
  $15 \times 22\frac{1}{8}$                                                                                   E.1187–1931

**4** INTERMEZZO VI. The descent of Apollo and Bacchus together with Rhythm and Harmony (*La Discesa di Apollo e Bacco insieme col Ritmo e l'Armonia*).
  On the stage level ten singers are grouped. Above these mythological personages sit enthroned on clouds.
  $16 \times 21\frac{9}{16}$                                                                                   E.1189–1931

*These* Intermezzi, *descended from the simple* entr'actes *in fifteenth-century Italian revivals of Roman comedies, were presented in 1589 with the comedy* La Pellegrina *by Girolamo Bargagli. They were so impressive they became the subject of several commemorative books, and it is probable the engraving in Plate 6 was intended as an illustration to one of these books. The design for the 4th* Intermezzo *and a copy of the design for the 5th are in the Louvre; there are some costume designs by Buontalenti for the series in the Biblioteca Nazionale Centrale, Florence, and records of sums spent on the costumes in the Florentine State Archives.*

*An intermezzo was a pantomime which included madrigals, and some dancing. Soon afterwards the opera and the ballet began to evolve independently from this type of entertainment. The first real opera is generally held to have been Ottavio Rinuccini's* Dafne, *first performed in 1597. It was Rinuccini who wrote the libretto for the 1589* Intermezzi, *the music being by Marenzio and others, and the invention being by Giovanni de' Bardi. The marriage festivities at Florence in 1589 included masquerades, animal hunts, a sham sea-battle and three comedies. 'All the comedies', writes Mr James Laver, 'were enlivened by the same series of* Intermezzi *which were performed on May 2nd and 6th, and were repeated on May 13th for the benefit of the Venetian ambassadors.'* (Burlington Magazine, CCCLI, *p. 294, 1932.*)

BUONTALENTI, Bernardo, called Buontalenti delle Girandole (1536–1608).

5 Designs for the costumes of two female dancers, probably in the Florentine *Intermezzi* of 1589 (see Plates 3, 4 and 6).

*Pen and ink and water-colour;* $10\frac{3}{8} \times 11\frac{1}{16}$                E.614–1936
Given by the National Art Collections Fund.

*This drawing was long supposed to be by Vasari, whose name is inscribed in ink upon it; but in 1936 the style was discovered to be very like that of a drawing signed by Buontalenti in the Uffizi Gallery. It appeared reasonable then to associate it with Buontalenti's designs for the celebrated* Intermezzi *of 1589.*

*The ornament in the costumes, and the scalloped and tasselled fringes, and the plumes, are consciously artistic in the Mannerist style, and would not have been found on the ordinary clothes of the time. Below the kilted tunics are flimsy diaphanous-looking skirts, more suitable for dancing than the much heavier and stiffer skirts worn off the stage. In the seventeenth century such skirts became a little shorter, but the kilted effect and the fringes, and the plumes, remained peculiar to ballet costumes. Even the Mannerist ornament survived to some extent in the designs of Berain (see Plates 41–44). The wedge-heeled shoes, or chopines, on the other hand, are of a type that was in domestic use in Italy throughout the sixteenth century, and soon went out of fashion as the next century advanced.*

*Buontalenti was in the service of the Medici family of Florence for nearly sixty years. His range included the construction of gardens and fortifications, and the arrangement of funerals, festivities and firework displays—hence the nickname* delle Girandole.

CARACCI, Agostino (1557–1602), after Bernardo BUONTALENTI (1536–1608).

6 IL COMBATTIMENTO PITICO D'APOLLO. Apollo slaying the Python. A representation of the third of the *Intermezzi* performed at Florence in 1589 in honour of the marriage of the Grand Duke Ferdinand I of Tuscany with Christina of Lorraine.

*Engraving;* $9\frac{5}{8} \times 13\frac{7}{8}$                23088.8

*Some of the original drawings for the scenery and costumes of the* Intermezzi *of 1589 by Buontalenti are reproduced in Plates 3–5. This print by Agostino Caracci is based on Buontalenti's design for* Intermezzo III (E.1188–1931, *not reproduced), though the suspended figure of Apollo does not appear in the drawing and the composition is partly reversed. The print is a late impression published by Filippo Suchielli, Siena.*

*It was not easy to represent snakes on the stage. In any case it seems that the idea of a serpent at this date was not necessarily equivalent to that of a snake. Milton's serpents in Pandemonium were 'complicated monsters' (Book X, 523), and included scorpions, asps, hydras and other creatures, while Satan himself was described as a Dragon larger than the Python of Delphi. From this it is clear that the Python was often conceived as a Dragon.*

CANTAGALLINA, Remigio (*c.*1582–*c.*1635), after Giulio PARIGI (worked 1580–1635).

7 PALAZZO DELLA FAMA. View of the stage with scenery and players in the first of the six *Intermezzi* performed at Florence in 1608 in honour of the marriage of Cosimo

de'Medici (later Cosimo II of Tuscany) to the Princess Anna Magdalena of Austria. From a set of six.

*Etching; cut to* $7\frac{1}{4} \times 10\frac{5}{16}$                       E.610–1949

*The Renaissance loggia of the Palace is flanked by ruins, and relieved by what was evidently a back-cloth, painted in light tones to suggest a long landscape vista.*


ANONYMOUS (early 17th century).

8–14    Designs (7) for costumes in ballets or intermezzi. Florentine or French, *c.*1600–1620. From a series of twenty designs by the same hand mounted in a volume (E.481–500–1936).

*Pen, ink and water-colour*

**8**    A man in the role of Hercules.
$9\frac{3}{8} \times 6$                           E.482–1936

**9**    A man in the role of a prince or king.
$9\frac{5}{8} \times 6\frac{15}{16}$                        E.483–1936

**10**    A woman in clothes decorated with sea-weed and coral. Inscribed in pencil in a later hand *Thetis*.
$10\frac{3}{8} \times 5\frac{15}{16}$                        E.489–1936

**11**    A woman with castanets.
$9\frac{3}{4} \times 7\frac{1}{8}$                          E.492–1936

**12**    A man wearing slashed hose, a crown and a conical hat. Inscribed in pencil in a later hand *Le Roi Periandie*.
$8\frac{13}{16} \times 6\frac{7}{8}$                        E.494–1936

**13**    A woman wearing a divided skirt and carrying a bow. Inscribed in pencil in a later hand *Nymphe*.
$9\frac{1}{2} \times 6\frac{11}{16}$                        E.497–1936

**14**    A man in the role of a satyr. Inscribed in pencil in a later hand *Satire*.
$10\frac{1}{16} \times 7\frac{1}{4}$                        E.500–1936

*These coloured drawings are mounted with thirteen similar ones in a volume bound in vellum and stamped in gold with a design incorporating the royal arms of France which was in use between c. 1635 and c. 1670. The volume was formerly in the possession of Sir Henry Bunbury, 7th baronet, soldier and antiquary (1778–1860).*

*A note attached to the fly-leaf says that the drawings were 'till the period of the revolution, preserved in the Garde Meuble at Paris. In the course of the troubles, they became the property of the Mob that pillaged the royal repository, and, when discovered, were in so bad a state, round the edges, as to require remounting.' The note then goes on to say the designs were made for the costumes of actors performing before Francis I and Henry VIII at the Field of the Cloth of Gold (1520). They are, nevertheless, about a century later in date, and instead of being connected in some way with the School of Fontainebleau as the note suggests, are probably by an Italian artist working at the French court early in the reign of Louis XIII. There is in E.497–1936 (Plate 13), for instance, a clear debt to the Florentine intermezzi of the late sixteenth and early seventeenth centuries.*

*The Hercules costume (Plate 8) is interesting as being an early example of the combination of a tunic and an imitation of the Roman* lorica *from which the later stylised 'heroic' costumes evolved. The feminine costumes may have been intended for young men wearing*

*masks. It was not customary for women to perform in ballets at the French court until
1654.*


CALLOT, Jacques (1592–1635), after Giulio PARIGI (worked *c.* 1580–1635).

15 – 17  Views of the three intermezzi in *La Liberazione di Tirreno e d'Arnea*, performed at
the wedding of Ferdinando Gonzaga, Duke of Mantua, and Caterina de'Medici in the
theatre of the Uffizi Palace, Florence, on 6th February, 1617.

*Etchings*
Purchased from the funds of the Enthoven Bequest.

**15** First intermezzo, showing the inside of the theatre, dancers, spectators and the stage,
on which appears a glade with the volcano covering Typhoeus, the giant. Fourth
state.
$11\frac{3}{8} \times 8$                                                                                          E.2837–1962

**16** Second intermezzo, showing an inferno scene, with Pluto and infernal creatures.
Only state.
$8 \times 11\frac{3}{8}$                                                                                          E.2838–1962

**17** Third intermezzo, showing Amor and his court appearing in the clouds to interrupt
a combat. Only state.
$8 \times 11\frac{3}{8}$                                                                                          E.2839–1962

*The first of the series shows the inside of the theatre (Teatro Medici) designed by
Buontalenti (see Plates 3–6) in 1586 within the Uffizi Palace; and it also shows how
many of the performances which included ballets at this period must have been produced.
Here semi-circular steps and curved ramps led from the stage into the auditorium, which
was raked. The performance was extended over the hall where the stalls and pit would now
be situated and was surrounded by promenading spectators.*

La Liberazione di Tirreno *was a* veglia *or drama, not an opera, with intermezzi. An
account of this* veglia *by a contemporary, Gioseffo Casato, tells us that after Typhoeus
was overthrown in the first scene there was a most beautiful ballet danced by twelve
gentlemen (who had emerged from the mountain destroyed by Jupiter) 'first on the stage
(palco) and then, by the same twelve dancers and by twelve ladies richly apparelled', in
the midst of the auditorium (teatro) where the Grand Duke danced among the gentlemen
and the Archduchess among the ladies. (Quoted by A. M. Nagler in* Theatre Research,
*vol. III, No. 1, 1961, pp. 11, 12.) This may well be what is illustrated in the print.*

*The second print in the series shows the second scene, with Pluto, two infernal judges
and various infernal creatures. The forms of these creatures are in the mediaeval tradition
but with something of the elegance of Mannerist* grotteschi *of the period. Presumably the
set was made of three wings on each side and a backcloth showing the castles and ruined
arches.*

*The third scene shows a battle in progress with musicians ranged along either side. The
backcloth in this case probably came at the far ends of the lines of musicians. This forty-
minute combat was stopped by Amor, who is shown descending on to the stage with his
court in cloud machines. A ballet like the one already described by Casato, only larger,
concluded* La Liberazione di Tirreno.

*The libretto was by Andrea Salvadori, the music by Marco da Gagliano, and the
designs for scenes and costumes by Giulio Parigi. The ballets and combats were invented and
directed by Agniolo Ricci. All these specialists were officials of the Tuscan ducal court.*

PARIGI, Alfonso, the Younger (died 1656).

18 Design for an inferno scene in the opera *Le Nozze degli Dei*, performed at the Pitti Palace, Florence, on 1st August, 1634.

*Pen, pencil and red chalk; $7\frac{3}{4} \times 11\frac{3}{4}$*        E.251–1928

*The outlines of the drawing are indented and the back is dusted over with red chalk for tracing. This is one of Parigi's original designs from which Stefano Della Bella made the etchings noted below (Plates 19–21). But there are considerable differences between this composition and the finished etching, which is entitled* Scena Quinta d'Inferno *(24307.5: not reproduced). From the stage directions on the etched version it appears that the centaurs, lightly drawn in pencil in the foreground, and the infernal monsters performed some sort of dance together. Presumably the monsters shown in the air were to be dancers or puppets in suspension, or arriving on the stage by means of suspension.*

*The scenery and costumes used for this opera, with its choreographic episodes, were almost certainly designed by Alfonso Parigi the Younger.*


DELLA BELLA, Stefano (1610–1664), after Alfonso PARIGI the Younger (died 1656).

19 – 21 Etchings (3) from a series of seven, showing ballet scenes in the opera *Le Nozze degli Dei*, performed in the courtyard of the Pitti Palace, Florence, in honour of the marriage of Ferdinand II of Tuscany and Vittoria of Urbino, 1st August, 1634. Published in 1637.

*Etchings*

19 SCENE III. The Garden of Venus.
$8 \times 11\frac{1}{2}$        24307.3

20 SCENE IV. A Seashore.
$8 \times 11\frac{3}{8}$        24307.4

21 SCENE VI. The Heavens.
$8\frac{1}{8} \times 11\frac{1}{4}$        24307.6

*Scenes III and IV show Alfonso Parigi's treatment of typical Florentine conventions, the first for a garden, the second for a romantic landscape. Scene VI is unusual in having various levels for the performance screened by curtains and rusticated pillars.*

*In the designs of Giulio and Alfonso Parigi the stage sets for opera and ballet at Florence evolved from the limited and traditional conceptions of the sixteenth century, extended by Buontalenti, to a sharper and more veristic specification of scene. In the later works of Giacomo Torelli (1608–1678) in Venice and Paris the vistas in the scenery began to be made spokewise from the centre of the stage, which device became one of the characteristics of the Baroque theatre. Torelli too was responsible for the gradual combination of various traditional devices, Florentine, Venetian and French, into the formulae accepted for many of the opera-ballet sets of the next hundred and fifty years (see P. Bjurström,* Giacomo Torelli, *Stockholm, 1961, pp. 198–211).*

*The type of skirted and plumed costume, which in later ballets and operas of the seventeenth century became much more conventionalised, appears in Scenes III and VI. Some of the dancers in Scene IV are shown executing caprioles or 'capers'.*

ANONYMOUS (middle of 17th century)

**22** Design for the costume of a dancer in the role of an Amazon in a *ballet de cour*. French, *c.* 1650. From a collection of forty-six drawings of costumes and ballets by various seventeenth-century hands mounted in a volume (E.1291–1336–1936).

*Pen, ink, water-colour and gold;* $10\frac{5}{8} \times 6\frac{11}{16}$ E.1311–1936

*The design shows a dancer holding a term, the numerous breasts of which suggest it is meant to be Artemis, or Diana of Ephesus, a renowned goddess of fertility. Ephesus, according to legend, was founded by Amazons, who were sometimes represented wearing* chitons *girded above and below their waists, like the dark-toned garment shown in that position and coloured red in the design. The skirt worn under the red garment is coloured pale yellow with a decoration in grey lines, and may be meant to correspond to the lower part of the* tunica *of the Classical world.*

*This combination of garments was evidently used for dancing women in the Florentine intermezzi of the sixteenth century, and not necessarily for Amazons (see Plate 5). If, however, we add to such attributes the winged helmet, the term and the masculine appearance of the dancer, it looks as if the costume was intended here to be that of an Amazon. The masculine appearance may have been otherwise intentional, since at this date women of the court still took no part in the ballets danced by courtiers, the female roles being adopted by youths wearing masks. The use of the mask declined after 1654 when court ladies influenced by Italian operas first appeared in a* ballet de cour, *and were no longer prohibited from doing so thereafter.*

*As to the authorship of the drawing, there can be little doubt that it, and at least seven others in the Victoria and Albert Museum, E.1291–1336–1936, are the work of the artist whose designs for the* Ballet du Roi des Fêtes de Bacchus *(1651) repose in the Bibliothèque Nationale in Paris. These designs are ascribed to Gissey by Decurgis and Reymond in* Le Décor de Théâtre en France *(Paris, 1954), but they differ fundamentally from the drawings in the Victoria and Albert Museum (see Plates 24–29 and 35). The Paris designs have also been attributed to Charles or Henri de Beaubrun; and to Hans, Pierre or Nicolas Dumonstier (see Per Bjurström,* Giacomo Torelli, *Stockholm, 1961, p. 127, note 28).*

*With the passing of the vogue for the* ballet mélodramatique *and the rise of the* ballet à entrées *from 1620, many of the French productions of this period were performed in the centre of a hall with the audience sitting around and some of them intermittently taking part, so that the need for stage sets seldom arose and few designs for scenery have survived.*

DELLA BELLA, Stefano (1610–1664).

**23** A series of plans of the figures in an equestrian ballet performed by night in 1652 before the Archdukes Ferdinand Charles (1628–1662) and Sigismund Francis (1630–1665) and the Archduchess Anne of Tuscany in the arena next to the Grand-Ducal Palace at Florence. From *Combattimento E Balletto A Cavallo Rappresentato di Notte A'Serenissimi Arciduchi* etc., Florence, 1652.

*Etching;* $12\frac{1}{8} \times 9$ Library: Piot Collection 896

*This print is one of the illustrations to the text of an entertainment given at Florence in 1652, in which the equestrian ballet followed a sham equestrian battle, also geometrically planned, both being composed by Cavaliere Tommaso Guidoni. There was a 'machine' consisting of a grampus which turned itself into a ship, the invention of Ferdinando Tacca. The verses recited were by Benedetto Rigoli; and the costumes, scenery, car of Neptune and other ornaments were designed by Alfonso Parigi.*

*Horse ballets of this kind were common features of Italian and French open-air enter-tainments and pageants. The tradition persists to this day in the equestrian exercises of the haute école of Vienna, with their complicated passaging and caracolling.*

GISSEY, Henry (1621–1673), attributed to.

24 – 27 Designs (4) for costumes in court ballets. French, *c*. 1660–1673. From a collection of forty-six drawings of costumes and ballets by various hands mounted in a volume (E.1291–1336–1936). Inscribed (except E.1295) in pen with indications of materials and colours etc.

*Pen, ink and wash*

**24** Male dancer in female clothes; wearing mask, plumed headdress and bodice with exaggerated and scalloped basques.
$8\frac{1}{2} \times 5\frac{1}{2}$        E.1291–1936

**25** Male dancer in pseudo-oriental costume, with fur hat.
$8\frac{1}{4} \times 6$        E.1297–1936

**26** Suivant de Diane. Male dancer wearing a plumed hat and a *tonnelet* and holding a spear in his left hand.
$9\frac{3}{16} \times 7\frac{1}{16}$        E.1298–1936

**27** Bird costume, consisting of a skirt with wings, feet and headpiece.
$5\frac{3}{4} \times 6\frac{9}{16}$        E.1295–1936

*Here the attribution to Gissey is tentative, but if it is correct, then these drawings, together with nine others by the same hand in the volume referred to are of great import-ance in the history of the theatre.*

*Gissey was the son of a sculptor. He held the appointment of* Dessinateur de la Chambre et du Cabinet du Roi *from 1660 to 1673, in which post he was responsible for designing the King's fêtes and ballets. Under the patronage of Louis XIV the artists of the* ballet de cour *went to the extremes of contemporary fantasy, at the same time developing notably French characteristics, one of which, illustrated by the design for the clothes of a follower of Diana (Plate 26) was a style of orderly excess in ornamental details. These basques, tassels and fringes came to France by way of the Florentine intermezzi, but were used by Gissey with prolific invention in his designs for Louis XIV's Carrousel of 1662. Under Jean Berain the Elder, his disciple and successor as* Dessinateur du Cabinet, *Gissey's manner underwent a starching and formalising process in harmony with the changed tone of court life from about 1680 to 1715.*

*The design for the bird costume is a lingering example of the grotesque type of ballet dress popular under Louis XIII.*

GISSEY, Henry (1621–1673), attributed to.

**28** Design for the costume of a dancer in the role of an apothecary in a *ballet de cour*. French, *c*. 1660. From a collection of forty-six drawings of costumes and ballets by various hands mounted in a volume (E.1291–1336–1936). Inscribed in ink with notes on materials and colours.

*Pen, ink and water-colour;* $11 \times 7\frac{13}{16}$        E.1309–1936

*The costume is in the burlesque style for a comedy ballet of the kind that had been popular under Louis XIII, but which passed out of favour as the century lengthened, particularly in France where elegance and formality reigned. Burlesque characters were*

29. HENRY GISSEY (attributed to). Design for a dancer in a *ballet de cour*, *c.* 1660.
Coloured drawing.

frequently dressed in somewhat out-of-date costumes and it will be noticed that though the sleeves and epaulettes are purely fantastic the general style of the clothes belongs to the early years of the century. The hat is in the form of an alembic on a stove, in the middle of which, just above the man's left eye, a fire is shown burning. The jacket is coloured chestnut brown, and according to one of the annotations was made of satin. The doublet and breeches are black with gold linings showing through the rows of slashes.

GISSEY, Henry (1621–1673), attributed to.

**29**  Design for the costume of a male dancer in a leading role in a *ballet de cour*. French, *c*. 1660. From a collection of sixty-six drawings of costumes and ballets by various hands mounted in a volume (E.1291–1336–1936).

*Pen, ink, water-colour and gold; 9 × 6$\frac{1}{16}$*                     E.1310–1936

This drawing may represent *Louis XIV at the age of about twenty-two, that is to say c. 1660, nine years before his premature corpulence and apparent changes of temperament had influenced him to give up taking part in court frivolities.*

*The doublet has large basques falling over a flared* tonnelet, *a peculiar skirt-like garment descended presumably from the Roman* tunica, *and by this time an important feature in male theatrical dress. At first it was more commonly worn in the heroic style with a jacket or doublet imitating the old Roman* lorica (*see Plate 8*). *Here is an early use of the* tonnelet *worn independently of martial costume.*

*To raise the standard of musical dancing in France by comparison with the standard prevailing in the Italian Opera company,* Louis XIV *founded* L'Académie Nationale de la Danse *in 1661. In 1669–1672 this institution was enlarged to become* L'Académie Nationale de Musique et de la Danse *and from thenceforward was generally referred to in Paris as the* Opéra.

ANONYMOUS (middle of 17th century).

**30**  Design for a choreographic composition and the costumes of nine men holding a caduceus in each hand. French, *c*. 1660. From a collection of forty-six drawings of costumes and ballets by various hands mounted in a volume (E.1291–1336–1936).

*Pen, ink and wash; 5$\frac{3}{8}$ × 10$\frac{1}{2}$*                     E.1325–1936

*The slashed breeches and sleeves of the eight dancers surrounding the central figure differ very little from those in general use in the earlier part of the century. But the voluminous shirt-sleeves and periwig of the central dancer suggest a date not much earlier than 1660. From the large crown he wears it looks as if he was intended to represent Louis XIV as a young man playing a leading rôle in a* ballet de cour. *His high plumed headdress and the ornamental details on his* tonnelet *are typical of the style associated with Henry Gissey, who may have been the author of the drawing.*

ANONYMOUS (middle of 17th century).

**31**  Designs (4) for costumes and choreographic compositions in a dance of savages or American Indians in a *ballet de cour*. French, *c*. 1660. From a series of nineteen similar

**32**  designs (E.1317–1324–1936 and E.1326–1336–1936) in a collection of forty-six drawings of costumes and ballets by various hands mounted in a volume (E.1291–1336–1936).

**33**  *Pencil; average size 7$\frac{1}{8}$ × 10$\frac{1}{2}$*                     E.1317, 1322, 1332, 1335–1936

**34** *The most exotic and interesting type of savage known to the seventeenth century was the American Indian, and semi-nude 'Indian' dancers clothed with imitation leaves or weeds were very popular in French ballets from well back in the seventeenth century until the end of the* ancien régime *(cf. the design for a satyr in Plate 14).*

*One of these drawings depicts the dancers in open order performing* caprioles, *but the other three, and many of the rest in the series, show how acrobatic this style of male dancing could be. Even today acrobatic* tableaux *retain their appeal more noticeably in France than anywhere else. Presumably such dances were performed by professional dancers.*


GISSEY, Henry (1621–1673), attributed to.

**35** Design for the costume of a lictor in the group of *Estafiers Romains* in the Carrousel held in Paris in June, 1662, to celebrate the birth of the Dauphin. From a collection of forty-six drawings of costumes and ballets by various seventeenth-century hands mounted in a volume (E.1291–1336–1936).

*Pen, ink, wash, water-colour and gold;* $9\frac{1}{16} \times 4\frac{1}{16}$            E.1312–1936

*In ancient Rome the lictors, bearing fasces consisting of an axe in a bundle of rods, attended upon the magistrates and carried out the punishments awarded to offenders. The 'Roman' group taking part in Louis XIV's Carrousel included three* estafiers *or lictors on foot, and this design corresponds in reverse to the figure of the foremost lictor in the group engraved by* Chauveau *for the* Courses de Testes et de Bague faites par le Roi etc., *by Charles Perrault, a record of the Carrousel of 1662 printed at the* Imprimerie Royale *in 1670. The designs for the costumes of the Carrousel (with the exception of the American quadrille by Carlo Vigarani) were by Henry Gissey,* Dessinateur du Cabinet du Roi, *then at the height of his career.*

*In the text of the 1670 volume the colours of the lictors are red, silver and gold. In this design the plumes, the skirted tunic, the upper row of piccadils on the* lorica, *the middle portions of the boots and a few other details are coloured in light red with dark red depths and ornaments in gold, and the other parts of the costume are drawn in ink and wash only, with decorations touched in with gold.*


CHAUVEAU, François (1613–1676), after Henry GISSEY (1621–1673).

**36** Philippe duc d'Orléans, called *Monsieur*, as the King of Persia in Louis XIV's Carrousel held in Paris in June, 1662. From a series of engravings (28654.8, 28654.9, 29530.1–19) taken from the *Courses de Testes et de Bague faites par le Roi et par les Princes et Seigneurs de sa Cour En l'année 1662*, by Charles Perrault, printed at the *Imprimerie Royale* in 1670.

*Engraving;* $11\frac{1}{2} \times 10\frac{1}{4}$            29530.6

*The Carrousel of 1662 began as a procession, mainly equestrian, from the Hôtel de Vendôme, to an amphitheatre constructed for several thousands of spectators behind the Tuileries. It consisted of about five hundred persons forming five quadrilles, the first led by Louis XIV and the others by royal princes, including* Monsieur.

*Philippe duc d'Orléans (1640–1701), the second son of Louis XIII, was a man greatly addicted to entertainments of every kind, particularly ballets; and also to homosexual intrigues. Since pederasty flourished at that time in Persia, his role as an imaginary king of Persia seems too appropriate to have happened by accident. The other chief participants also had suitable roles; Louis XIV himself was a Roman emperor, and the duc de Guise, an adventurous and romantic prince, was an American savage king.*

Monsieur *is shown wearing a coat, described in the text as of silver brocade embroidered with silver and decorated with roses His cloak was of rose brocade embroidered with silver and sewn with pearls, and his hat in the Persian style was of rose brocade decorated with gold, rubies and pearls. The plumes on the hat were white and rose-coloured, the hose grey, the boots, of the same substance as the coat, decorated with silver brocade, rubies and rose and white ribbons. The harness was also of rose and silver brocade decorated with rubies, pearls and rose and white ribbons in an equally frivolous style. All the 'gems' were probably imitation.*

*Louis XIV's Carrousel included a procession, a parade in the amphitheatre and two days of jousting and horsemanship, and was related in parts to the horse ballets held in Italy (see Plate 23), though on a grander scale. It became the model for most of the other carrousels in Europe held during the late seventeenth and early eighteenth centuries.*

SILVESTRE, Israel (1621–1691).

**37** The performance of the comedy *La Princesse d'Élide* in the series of entertainments called *Les Plaisirs de l'Isle Enchantée* in the grounds of the Palace of Versailles, on the 8th May, 1664. From *Les Plaisirs de l'Isle Enchantée*, etc., Paris, 1673–1674.

*Etching;* $11\frac{1}{8} \times 16\frac{3}{4}$          Library

*Molière's verse play,* La Princesse d'Élide, *took place on the second day of the entertainments, and ended with a ballet of four shepherds and four shepherdesses, who also sang in chorus. While they danced, a mechanical tree came up above the orchestra holding eight violinists and eight flautists disguised as fauns. The passages played by these musicians were replied to by the orchestra beneath them. Here the play, not the ballet, is shown in progress.*

*The scenery was designed by Carlo Vigarani, son of Gaspare Vigarani of Modena, who succeeded Torelli as stage designer and engineer at the court of Louis XIV. The king and members of the court are seen in the foreground.*

SILVESTRE, Israel (1621–1691).

**38** The Island of Alcine in the ballet *Le Palais d'Alcine* performed on the third day in the series of entertainments called *Les Plaisirs de l'Isle Enchantée*, 9th May, 1664. From *Les Plaisirs de l'Isle Enchantée*, etc., Paris, 1673–1674.

*Etching;* $10\frac{3}{4} \times 16\frac{1}{2}$          Library

*The ballet was arranged on a scene from* Orlando Furioso *by the Duc de Saint-Aignan, the music being by Lully. The scene was designed by Carlo Vigarani, son of Gaspare Vigarani of Modena, and was constructed in the open air on one of the lakes at Versailles.*

*Alcine is shown borne forward on a sea monster accompanied by two nymphs, Célie and Dircé on dolphins. To the right of them is a long rocky 'island', on which a row of violinists perform; and on the opposite side is a similar construction, on which trumpeters and tymballers are playing. In the middle distance is the enchanted palace on another 'island'. At the end of the sixth entrée the island of Alcine was destroyed in a grand firework display.*

WORM, Johannes (*c.* 1649–?), attributed to.

**39**  BALLET DES QUATRE GÉANTS ET QUATRE NAINS. Dutch, second half of the seventeenth century.

*Engraving; cut to* 6½×9¼                              E.3080–1938

*This engraving is signed by J. (?) Worm, about whom very little is known; and it bears the serial number 1550, which should mislead nobody. The style is Dutch, and the date probably about 1680.*

*There is evidently a close connection here with* Les Plaisirs de l'Isle Enchantée *of 1673–1674 (see Plates 37, 38), for the print appears to illustrate the first* entrée *in the* Ballet du Palais d'Alcine *consisting of a dance by the four giants Manceau, Vagnard, Pesan and Joubert and the four dwarfs Vagnard, Tutin and the Des Airs brothers. It is possible that a Dutch version of the* Plaisirs *volume came out about 1680.*

*The costumes are in the* Commedia dell'Arte *style for the dwarfs, and in a semi-heroic style for the giants, and there is no reason to suppose that the ones originally worn at Versailles were much different.*

KÜSEL, Matthaus (1629–1681), after Lodovico Ottavio BURNACINI (1636–1707).

**40**  Illustration of the ballet in *Il Pomo d'Oro*, Vienna, 1668, the text of an opera by Francesco di Filippo Sbarra (1611–1668), as performed in Vienna in 1668 at the wedding of the Emperor Leopold I and Margherita, daughter of Philip IV of Spain.

*Engraving;* 10⅜×17½                         Library: Piot Collection 452

*The ballet came at the end of the opera. In the sky cherubs and Olympians are shown, painted apparently on the same back-cloth as the tritons and sirens who are represented in the sea. The clothes of the dancers are in the 'heroic' style, evolved for such entertainments from Roman military costume.*

*Lodovico Burnacini was the son of Giovanni Burnacini (d. 1655) who built a theatre at Vienna in 1652 and designed the scenery used in it. During the second half of the seventeenth century his son Lodovico became the leading stage designer in Vienna, where the theatre, and opera especially, began to flourish under the patronage of the Emperor Leopold I.*

BERAIN, Jean Louis (1637–1711), Studio of.

**41**  Design for the costume of a male dancer with castanets, *c.* 1681.

*Pen, ink and water-colour, touched with gold, on vellum;* 7¾×5¼                   8898.3

*Probably a fair copy made by a studio assistant from a rough drawing by Berain. It corresponds to an outline drawing of the same subject in reverse from the studio of Berain in the* Musée de l'Opéra *(see* Les Costumes de l'Opéra *by Carlos Fischer, Paris, 1931, p. 47). Also it bears a close relation to the print after Berain showing the costume of Endymion in the ballet* Le Triomphe de l'Amour *of 1681 (see* Das Bühnenkostüm *by Max von Boehn, Berlin, 1921, p. 328).*

*Interesting features in the costume are the large basques on the jacket decorated with ornate floral motifs in a style suggesting marquetry of the period, and to which Berain gave currency in every department of practical art. The headdress consisting of a bonnet with vertical plumes is also characteristic of French theatrical male costume at the end of the seventeenth century.*

DOLIVAR, Jean (1641–169?), after Jean Louis BERAIN (1637–1711).

42, 43 Illustrations (2) of costumes worn in the ballet of *Le Triomphe de l'Amour* performed at St. Germain-en-Laye in 1681.

One of the nymphs in the *suite d'Orithis*. Third state of the plate.

**42** *Engraving; cut to* $10\frac{13}{16} \times 7\frac{3}{8}$          E.21424-1957

An Indian. Second or third state of the plate.

**43** *Engraving; cut to* $10\frac{3}{4} \times 7\frac{1}{2}$          E.21423-1957
Given by Worth Ltd. in association with Paquin Ltd.

*These impressions have been taken from copper-plates on which the original background details were altered.*

*The verse parts of* Le Triomphe de l'Amour *were by Quinault: the ballet consisted of numerous entrées with music by Lulli. All the costumes and the scenery of the entertainment were after designs by Berain. At the first performance of* Le Triomphe de l'Amour *given by the Dauphin on 21st January, 1681, at St. Germain-en-Laye, professional dancers like Mesdemoiselles Desmartins and La Fontaine of the* Académie Royale *took part in the entertainment with the* Princesse de Conti *and other ladies of the court. From then onwards the custom of having men in certain female roles in court performances was abandoned.*

Le Triomphe de l'Amour *was later first performed in Paris at the* Opéra *on 6th May, 1681.*

**44** BERAIN, Jean Louis (1637-1711), Studio of.

Design for the costume of a female dancer with castanets, *c.* 1685.

*Pen and wash;* $8\frac{3}{16} \times 6\frac{1}{8}$          8898.20

*Probably a fair copy made by a studio assistant from a rough drawing by Berain. It has a close similarity in the pose of the figure, but not in the details of the costume, to an outline drawing from the studio of Berain in the* Musée de l'Opéra (*see* Les Costumes de l'Opéra *by Carlos Fischer, Paris, 1931, p. 24).*

*The hard, metallic quality of his design, so typical of Berain, is emphasised by the stiff skirt, the inlaid effect of the ornamental patterns, and the pastes or semi-precious stones punctuating every part.*

**45** BERAIN, Jean Louis (1637-1711), attributed to.

Design for stage scenery representing an inferno.

*Pen and water-colour;* $13 \times 18\frac{1}{2}$          E.1028-1921
Presented by Mr. W. Barclay Squire, F.S.A., through the National Art Collections Fund.

*This drawing was formerly supposed to be Berain's preliminary study for the scenery in the last act of Lulli's opera* Armide et Renaud, *produced on 15th February, 1686, at the Paris Opera House. The last act of the opera included a ballet, and ended with the destruction of the palace of Armide. But the drawing reproduced here does not seem to relate to such an incident. It dates from the same period however, at which time Berain was stage-designer at the* Opéra. *A very similar drawing, in the* Archives Nationales, Paris, *is reproduced in* Le Décor de Théâtre en France *by Decugis and Reymond, Paris, 1953, Chapter IV, pl. 31.*

*The wide open, flat-headed monster mouth was a traditional feature in infernal scenes. Its iconography can be traced back through the paintings of Hieronymus Bosch to mediaeval mystery plays and wall-paintings of hell.*

CHEREAU, François (1688–1729), after Robert LEVRAC-TOURNIÈRES (1667–1752).

**46** Half-length portrait of the dancer and choreographer Guillaume Louis Pécourt (1653–1729) with a dance score open before him; *c.* 1710.

*Engraving; cut to* 16½×11⅝               E.191–1960
Given by Mr. Edgar Seligman.

*The title describes Pécourt as a royal pensioner, a composer of ballets for the* Académie Royale de Musique (*the formal name for the* Opéra), *and dancing master to the Duchess of Burgundy. Since the engraver was born in 1688 and the duchess died in 1712, the date of the print should be between* c. *1708 and* c. *1712. It is a good example of the ornate, definitive style of line-engraving perfected by the Drevet family in the early eighteenth century.*

*Pécourt's career began with his appearance in* Cadmus *in 1674 at the* Opéra, *where in due course he became* maître de ballet, *maintaining a reputation for dancing important roles in* Thésée, Athis, Persée, *and other opera-ballets until his retirement from the stage in 1703. He was also a composer of court ballets and held the appointment of dancing master to the royal pages. A year after his retirement the* Recüeil de dances contenant un tres grand nombre des meillieures Entrées de Ballet de Mr. Pecour, *with engraved plates of choreographic scores recording dances invented by him, was published by Feuillet in Paris (see Plate 47). This volume was followed a few years later by a supplementary* recüeil *of Pécourt's dances, also published by Feuillet.*

*The portrait here shows Pécourt wearing stage clothes or what was sometimes called gala costume. In La Bruyère's* Caractères *he is referred to under the pseudonym of Bathylle in Chapter III,* Des Femmes. '*Prenez Bathylle, Lélie,' says La Bruyère (Lélie being a pseudonym for the daughter of President Brisu): 'où trouverez-vous, je ne dis pas dans l'ordre des chevaliers que vous dédaignez, mais même parmi les farceurs, un jeune homme qui s'élève si haut en dansant, et qui fasse mieux la cabriole? Voudriez-vous le sauteur Cobus, qui, jetant ses pieds en avant, tourne une fois en l'air avant que de tomber a terre? Ignorez-vous qu'il n'est plus jeune? Pour Bathylle, dites-vous, la presse y est trop grande; et il refuse plus de femmes qu'il n'en agrée.'*

*Thus the sneers of a famous man of letters survive as the most accessible memorial of a gifted artist, no less talented probably in other ways than La Bruyère himself.*

ANONYMOUS (first quarter of 18th century).

**47** Part of a canary for two male dancèrs, executed by M. Pissetot and M. Chevrier in the opera *Dido*. Page 161 in *Recüeil de Dances contenant un tres grand nombres des meillieures Entrées de Ballet de Mr. Pecour* (sic) etc., by Raoul Auger Feuillet, Paris, 1704.

*Etching;* 9⅛×6⅛                 Library

*The etched page is reproduced to show the style of a choreographic score under Louis XIV, during which period Guillaume Louis Pécourt (1653–1729) was a famous dancer and choreographer (see Plate 46).*

*This dance was in 6/8 time, the passage recorded here being about halfway through it. The continuous lines supporting the hieroglyphics represent the tracks of the dancers across the stage, and could be straight or curved: here they are straight. At the top of the page underneath the melodic notation the two semi-circular symbols represent the two dancers, who begin with a whole turn to the right and to the left respectively, and proceed down the stage opposite each other. In the third bar (the bars are marked by short lines at intervals across the tracks) the dancers move inwards, their tracks cross, and they change sides on* the stage, proceeding onwards with pirouettes (indicated by semi-circular spirals). At the bottom of the page the eye is led by dashes to the return tracks over the same ground to the end of the passage. The symbols at each last bar on either side represent an entrechat.

ABBATI, Pietro Giovanni (worked first half of eighteenth century), after Ferdinando GALLI, called DA BIBIENA (1657–1743).

**48** Design for a stage set. Plate 5 in a series of seventy plates entitled *Varie Opere di Prospettiva Inventate da Ferdinando Galli* etc., Bologna, *c.* 1707.

*Etching; 10 × 10⅛*           E.1748–1930

*The interest of this print is that it records an early example of a design for the* scena per angolo *or scene with diagonal perspectives. It was the application of diagonal perspective to theatre design by Ferdinando Galli at Bologna in 1703 that permitted the eighteenth-century theatre artists to emphasise the illusion of scale, variety and distance in elaborate architectural fantasies. There appears to be no record of what this design was intended for: it would have served for an opera, and since many operas of this period were opera-ballets and included* ballet-divertissements, *the subject of opera scenery at the beginning of the eighteenth century clearly overlapped that of ballet scenery.*

*The Bibiena family, named after their town of origin in Italy, was a family of artists whose association with the theatre began soon after Ferdinando's employment at Parma from 1680. He worked in most of the Italian capitals and later as court architect and painter of festivities for the Emperor Charles VI at Vienna, in which post he was succeeded by one of his sons, Giuseppe (see Plate 56).*

PUSCHNER, Johann Georg (working *c.* 1720).

**49–55** Plates (7) showing theatrical dancers of all nations from *Deliciae Theatrales. Neue und Curieuse Theatralische Tantz-Schul* by Gregorio Lambranzi, a volume in two parts containing 101 plates engraved by Puschner from his own designs, published by Johann Jacob Wolrab, Nürnberg, 1716.

*Engravings*

**49** BOURÉE. *The pair shown here are peasants. When they have danced half their measure, the woman steals away to the background, and the man, not being able to see her, begins to lament. The woman then comes back unperceived behind him, takes him by the shoulders, twirls him around several times and thus renews the dance with him.*

*The style of the costumes dates from the early seventeenth century, but has become conventionalised.*

*9 × 6½*           E.1218–1927

**50** CORRENTE. *The dancers are said here to be in Roman costume, that is in the 'noble' or 'heroic' style, to execute a corrente. The man wears an embroidered jacket with tabs, reminiscent of the Roman cuirass or* lorica, *worn over a* tonnelet *with a pleated skirt. The stiffened out-curving shape of the tabs and* tonnelet *together was the most curious feature of early eighteenth-century men's ballet (and opera) costumes in the 'noble' style. It exaggerated a tendency already noticeable in the Roman costumes of Louis XIV's Carrousel of 1662.*

*9 × 6½*           E.1235–1927

**51** SCHARAMUZA. *Scaramouche brings on to the stage two small baskets, in which are concealed two small scaramouches. He then dances a measure, at the end of which he opens the baskets and is surprised to see what they contain. The two little scaramouches spring out, kick him, throw him to the ground and dance together to the same aria; after which Scaramouche gets up and puts the two little scaramouches back into the baskets, and walks off with long strides.*

*The costume is the traditional one of Scaramouche in the Italian* Commedia dell'Arte, *although at this date he often wore knee-breeches instead of trousers.*

$9 \times 6\frac{1}{2}$                                                                          E.1239–1927

**52** DETA. *Presumably the other leg and the rest of the body of each of these dancers was concealed behind a wing of the setting. The forms above the breeches are described as hats.*

$9 \times 6\frac{1}{2}$                                                                          E.1241–1927

**53** NARCISIN. *Both dancers wear large straw hats and carry on their faces cut orange skins for false eyes. After they have come running on to the stage, the man kisses his partner, who twirls away from him. He follows, and she slaps him—and so on.*

*The man's costume and its female counterpart derive from the character of Narcisin di Malembergo in the* Commedia dell'Arte.

$9 \times 6\frac{1}{2}$                                                                          E.1259–1927

**54** GALIARDO. *The costume of the dancer is stated to be that of an English sailor. It is described as being decorated with a quantity of wooden spoons, hung in rows on the jacket and from the bottoms of the knee-breeches.*

$9 \times 6\frac{1}{2}$                                                                          E.1287–1927

**55** ZURLO BACHO. *This dance seems to have involved a kind of sitting* pirouette *alternating with springs in the air, possibly resembling the kicking dance performed by warriors in* Prince Igor.

*The clothes are the ordinary clothes of the time.*

$9 \times 6\frac{1}{2}$                                                                          E.1302–1927

*Lambranzi's* Dancing School *is probably the earliest book dealing entirely with theatrical and ballet dancing, and not with dancing as a social accomplishment.*

PFEFFEL, Johann Andreas (the Elder) (1674–1748), after Giuseppe GALLI, called DA BIBIENA (1696–1757).

**56** Design for a stage set, *c.* 1720. Plate 30 in the series of fifty-five plates entitled *Architetture e Prospettive*, Augsburg, 1740.

*Engraving;* $13\frac{3}{8} \times 20\frac{1}{8}$                                                                          E. 1796–1930

*It is not known what this design was intended for, though it seems likely that it was for an opera, and operas in those days often included intervals of ballet. In any case, it illustrates the type of scenery evolved by the Galli family in Italy and the German courts at various times throughout most of the eighteenth century. Here again is the diagonal perspective introduced on the stage by Ferdinando Galli (see Plate 48) and used by Giuseppe Galli to enrich and enlarge the ornate Baroque fantasies for which he was celebrated.*

*This print and others in the same series have an evenness of texture that gives no clue to just how the scenes were constructed on the stage—what was three-dimensional and what was painted in* trompe l'oeil *on back-cloth and flats. It is certain however that illusionist painting accounted for a good deal of the effect, and, since Italian artists of the period were more skilled in this craft than others, the most ambitious Baroque stage productions were seldom seen outside Italy and the central European courts where Italians like the Bibieni found employment. Nevertheless, Giuseppe's son Carlo (1728–1787) worked in France, England, the Netherlands, Stockholm and St. Petersburg, apart from the courts of Bayreuth, Berlin, Brunswick and Munich, and various Italian capitals. Giovanni Maria Galli the Younger worked in Prague from 1739 to 1769, and Giovanni Carlo in Lisbon, where he died in 1760. No other artist or dynasty of artists in the eighteenth century had quite such a powerful influence on the course of stage design as the Bibieni. Echoes of their style survive clearly enough in the Romantic scenery of Sanquirico (1780–1849) (see Plates 96 and 97).*

LIOR, P. (working second quarter of 18th century), attributed to.

**57** Design for the costume of a faun in a ballet. French *c.* 1744. *Inscribed in ink on the back* P Lior 1744.

*Pen, ink and water-colour;* $8\frac{1}{2} \times 5\frac{1}{4}$                                    E.23027–1957
Given by Worth Ltd. in association with Paquin Ltd.

*So far the name Lior has not been identifiable as that of an artist working in 1744, but the inscription on the back of the drawing looks more like a signature than anything else, and the explanation may be that someone of that name found employment for a time in making fair copies of original designs by other artists, such as Jean Baptiste Martin (working first half of eighteenth century). The drawing was acquired by the Museum alongside E.23028–1957 (Plate 58), and both appear to be by the same hand.*

*A good idea of J. B. Martin's style may be gained by referring to the* Gallerie des Modes et Costumes Français *(1778), or to the more accessible reprint of this work published in 1911–1914. Plate 104 in Volume II of the reprint shows a faun in the* Fête de Bacchus, *whose costume is conceived on similar lines to those of this drawing, although the Lior dancer is wearing buskins and the Martin dancer wears knee-breeches and shoes. The Martin design appears to have been worn by Laval and Gardel in* Vertumne et Pommone *at Versailles as late as 1763.*

*The basic colour of the costume (excluding leopard skin, green vine-leaves and gray plumes) is red, with yellow decorations.*

LIOR, P. (working second quarter of 18th century), attributed to.

**58** Design for the costume of a herald or trumpeter in an opera or ballet. French *c.* 1744.
*Pen, ink and water-colour;* $7\frac{1}{3} \times 6\frac{1}{2}$                                    E.23028–1957
Given by Worth Ltd. in association with Paquin Ltd.

*This drawing, together with E.23027–1957 (Plate 57), was found pasted down in a scrap-book among the records presented to the Department of Prints and Drawings by the Paris dress-making firm of Maison Worth. It is evidently by the same hand as E.23027–1957, which is inscribed 'P Lior 1744'.*

*The main colours shown are sky blue and white, the jacket and trumpet-banner being blue with white decorations, and the tonnelet and buskins being white with decorations mostly in blue. White and blue plumes alternate on the comb of the helmet. The sash is a darker shade of the prevailing blue.*

*In the middle years of the decade 1740–1750 the tonnelet on the male dancer spread out on supports to the farthest extent ever known before or since. Here this curious garment, descended from the underclothes of men in armour, has a width very nearly equal to the distance along the outstretched arms of the wearer. Impatience with the convention of the* tonnelet *may be said to date from the first publication in 1760 of* Lettres sur la Danse et les Ballets *by Jean Georges Noverre (1727–1809), the famous* maître de ballet. *In these he wrote that he was in favour of doing away with both tonnelets and panniers and of keeping to garments which revealed the dancers' figures.*

COCHIN, Charles Nicolas (the Younger) (1715–1790).

**59** View of the performance of *La Princesse de Navarre* in the riding school of the *Grandes Écuries* at Versailles on 23rd February, 1745, on the occasion of the marriage of Louis the Dauphin (son of Louis XV) with Marie Thérèse, Infanta of Spain. Engraved by Cochin from his own drawing.

*Engraving;* $29\frac{1}{4} \times 20\frac{7}{8}$                                              E.344–1905
Bequeathed by Mr. F. R. Bryan.

*The Duc de Richelieu was responsible for the festivities held on this occasion: the actual arrangements, however, were made by Monsieur de Bonneval,* Intendant et Controlleur Général de l'Argenterie, Menus Plaisirs et Affaires de la Chambre de sa Majesté.

La Princesse de Navarre *was written by Voltaire and was offered as a mixture of opera, comedy and tragedy, with the attractions of declamation, dancing and music. The piece included a number of songs and dances, and a* divertissement *at the end of it, here shown in progress. The scene has opened with a representation of the Pyrenees, which have disappeared at the Command of Love. In the place of the mountains is seen a temple consecrated to Cupid, who is seated on a throne at the centre. Four* quadrilles *completed the* divertissement. *The music was by Rameau (1683–1764).*

Louis XV *is shown sitting in the middle of the auditorium, with members of the Royal Family and ladies of the court. The performance began at six o'clock in the evening and finished at nine.*

*J. J. Rousseau in his* Confessions *gives an interesting account of how, in the winter of 1745–1746, Richelieu commissioned him to alter both Rameau's music and Voltaire's text in* La Princesse de Navarre *to suit the re-presentation of the opera at Versailles with the title of* Fêtes de Ramire.

ANONYMOUS (second quarter of 18th century).

**60** Designs for the costumes of a male and a female dancer in a comedy-ballet. French *c.* 1745.

*Black chalk and water-colour;* $8 \times 10\frac{3}{4}$                                    D.639–1889

*The woman's bonnet and hooped skirt are similar in outline to the ones in ordinary use during the 1740s. The man's clothes are based apparently on Italian peasant costume of the eighteenth century. Certain designs in this style seem to have included baggy breeches (as here) and tight breeches as worn off the stage (cf. Plate 61).*

HORÉOLLY — (worked first half of 18th century), after a drawing by Martin MARVIE (1713–1813).

**61** Camille Véronèse and François Riccoboni in the *Balet du Prince de Salerne*, performed at Fontainebleau in November, 1746. French, *c.* 1746.

*Engraving; cut to* $10\frac{1}{8} \times 6\frac{15}{16}$                                          24418.2

58. P. Lior (attributed to). Design for the costume of a trumpeter, c. 1722. Coloured drawing.

*François Riccoboni (1707–1772) was the son of Luigi Riccoboni (1675–1753) who directed the Italian company that gave performances of the* Commedia dell'Arte *at the* Théâtre des Italiens *in Paris, from 1716 onward. The ballet shown here, performed as an entertainment for the court at Fontainebleau, was a ballet-pantomime. This particular genre owed much to* Commedia dell'Arte *traditions and was greatly developed by François Riccoboni, and the Dutchman, Jean Baptiste de Hesse (1705–1769), at the* Théâtre des Italiens.

*The costumes, especially of the men, are intended to look like those of South Italian peasants. A similar high-crowned hat is to be seen in Plate 60. Here, however, the breeches are as close-fitting as those worn in everyday dress at this date.*

*The men and women lined up in the background are beating time with bats, or wands, very like the ones used for slapstick in the* Commedia dell'Arte.


BOQUET, Louis René (1717–1814).

**62**   Design for the costume of a princess in an opera or ballet, *c* 1750.

*Pen and water-colour over pencil;* $\sim \times 8\frac{1}{2}$            E.6–1956

*There is a costume design, not later than 1752, by Boquet in the* Bibliothèque de l' Opéra, Paris, *which shows two figures: a young prince wearing a cloak embroidered with peacock feathers and a hat decorated with ostrich plumes, in the act of sinking on his right knee at the feet of a princess before whom he has thrown his sceptre (see André Tessier,* Les Habits d'Opéra au XVIIIe Siècle. Louis Boquet etc., *in* Revue de l'Art Ancien et Moderne, *vol. XLIX, p. 15; and Carlos Fischer,* Les Costumes de l'Opéra, *Paris, 1931, pp. 86, 281). The figure of the princess in the Paris drawing is exactly similar to that of E.6–1956, and the incompleteness of the London drawing is shown by the fact that the right-hand edge of the paper passes through her train. It seems, therefore, that the figure of the prince has been cut away from E.6–1956, and that this drawing is either another version of the* Opéra *design made by Boquet for a court performance of the same opera or ballet; or it is a replica of the* Opéra *design made by his assistants for use in a wardrobe workshop. Since both versions are coloured and equally detailed it is difficult to be certain which of them is the earlier.*

*Boquet was much employed as a costume and scenery designer for the court entertainments organised by the* Intendance des Menus Plaisirs *at Versailles, Choisy and above all at Fontainebleau, from about 1750 until the Revolution. He held the office of* Dessinateur en chef des habits du Roi pour fêtes, spectacles et cérémonies *from 1764 to 1792, and was* Inspecteur Général des Menus Plaisirs *from c. 1770 until 1792. His parallel career at the* Opéra *seems to have begun around 1750 likewise, and his early designs in this field show the influence of Boucher who worked intermittently for the same institution. In 1759, after an interval of three or four years, Boquet succeeded Jean Baptiste Martin as designer-in-chief at the* Opéra, *and his later designs from c. 1760 to the end of the* ancien régime *are in a different style (see Plates 69, 70).*

*The Victoria and Albert drawing belongs to Boquet's earliest phase in theatrical design. The huge skirt embroidered in the Rococo style and distended over panniers to look like some enormous shell, was of course an exaggerated version of the contemporary fashion, brought to this degree of hyperbole by J. B. Martin in the 1750s. The masculine* tonnelet *developed to its greatest extent during the same period.*

MANELLI, Sante (working mid-eighteenth century), after Giovanni Carlo Sicinio GALLI, called DA BIBIENA (died 1760).

**63** RETIRO DELIZIOSO NEL SOGGIORNO IMPERIALE SUL COLLE PALATINO. Illustration of the stage setting for scenes VIII–XIII and the ballet in Act I of the opera *La Clemenza di Tito* as performed in honour of the birthday of King José of Portugal at the Teatro do Tejo, Lisbon, in 1755. Fourth plate in *La Clemenza di Tito*, etc., Lisbon, 1755.

*Engraving;* $6\frac{5}{8} \times 9\frac{3}{8}$                                      Library

*The engraver of the anonymous illustrations in the 1755 edition of this opera-libretto was presumably he whose name appears on the frontispiece, thus:* Sanctes Manelli Inc. Romae.

*Before being employed by King José (reigning 1750–1777), Giovanni Carlo Galli, the son of Francesco Galli, had worked as an architect and designer at Bologna. In Lisbon he designed the Teatro do Tejo, completed in April, 1755, and destroyed seven months later in the famous earthquake. The libretto of* La Clemenza di Tito, *a story of the Roman Emperor Titus, by Pietro Metastasio (1698–1782), was set to music by numerous composers: for this performance the music was composed by Antonio Mazzoni (c. 1718–after 1773), who had visited both Spain and Portugal some years before. The stage machinery was invented by Petronio Mazzoni, the scenery was designed by Giovanni Carlo Galli and the costumes by Antonio Bassi. The choreography of the dances was by Andrea Alberti, called* Il Tedeschino, *who was in the service of King José. Apart from one Frenchman, all the dancers in the ballets were Italians.*

*This set, representing the retreat of Titus on the Palatine Hill in Rome, was used for the later scenes in Act I and for the dance concluding that act. Dances also concluded the other two acts of the opera. While the design, with its peculiar fountain-columns, is conceived in a late Baroque style in which all the Bibieni practised, the background, rendered probably by a backcloth, shows a double staircase and steep ascent to a villa combining memories of the Villa d'Este gardens (1549) and the Spanish Steps (1723–1726) in Rome. The staircase leading to the eighteenth-century church of Bom Jesus near Braga in Portugal has the same architectural ancestry.*

THORNTHWAITE, J. (working 1771–1795), after James ROBERTS (c. 1725–1799).

**64** Signora Baccelli in the ballet *Les Amans Surpris*. From Bell's *British Theatre*, London, 15th May, 1781.

*Engraving; cut to* $6\frac{7}{8} \times 4\frac{1}{8}$                    Enthoven Collection

Les Amans Surpris *was first produced at the King's Theatre, London, on 16th December, 1780, with choreography by Simonet, ballet-master of the theatre.*

*The costume, with the skirt stretched over hoops, is a theatrical version of the contemporary vogue, with the skirt slightly shorter.*

*The process of shortening the skirts of female dancers began when La Camargo (Marie Anne de Cupis de Camargo, 1710–1770), best-remembered of all the eighteenth-century ballerinas and female exponent of the* entrechat, *had her own skirts shortened by a few inches in the second quarter of the century.*

**THORNTHWAITE, J.** (working 1771–1795), after James ROBERTS (*c.* 1725–1799).

**65** Gaëtan Vestris (1729–1808) as the Prince in the pantomime-ballet *Ninette à la Cour*. From Bell's *British Theatre*, London, 9th April, 1781.

*Engraving; cut to* $6\frac{9}{16} \times 3\frac{15}{16}$                    Enthoven Collection

*Ninette à la Cour first appeared in London at the King's Theatre on 22nd February, 1781, with choreography by Gaëtan Vestris based on that of Maximilien Gardel's ballet of the same name produced in Paris in 1778.*

*The costume is that of the period, with some theatrical inconsistencies to give the Prince a remote and fairy-tale appearance—such as the puffed sleeves, which are supposed to recall the slashed and busked sleeves of the Renaissance, and the hat with its high plumes, which was not far removed from the sort of hat worn in those days by a king in his Coronation robes.*

*It is interesting to see that the word pantomime is spelt, or misspelt, 'pantomine' as far back as this. Confusion arose in England about the exact meaning of the word, let alone its spelling, with the result that in Victorian times it was applied to the mixed productions of singing, dancing and burlesque associated with the Alhambra and Drury Lane Theatres.*

**BARTOLOZZI**, Francesco, R.A. (1727–1815) and Benedetto **PASTORINI** (*c.* 1746–*c.* 1803), after Nathaniel **DANCE**, R.A. (later Sir N. Dance-Holland, Bt.) (1734–1811).

**66** Marie Jean Augustin Vestris, known as Auguste Vestris, also as Vestr' Allard (1760–1842), son of Gaëtan Vestris, dancing a pirouette. Published 2nd April, 1781. Proof with date, but before aquatinting and titles (as quoted below). Inscribed in pencil in an old hand with verses as quoted below, and in ink on the right below the plate-mark; *M. Vestris at Vauxhall.*

*Etching and engraving;* $15\frac{1}{4} \times 1\frac{1}{2}$ .                    Enthoven Collection

*Auguste Vestris came over from Paris to London with his father Gaëtan Vestris for the 1780–1781 season, and a performance was given for his benefit at the King's Theatre, Haymarket, London, on 23rd February, 1781. It is curious to note that the second reading of Burke's Bill of Economic Reform, which was expected in the House of Commons on that day, was put off on account of the Haymarket performance, Burke himself observing that 'to a great part of that House, a dance was a much more important object than a war, and that the Opera House must be maintained whatever became of the country'. (See Mary Dorothy George, Catalogue of Political and Personal Satires in the British Museum, Vol. V, 1935, p. 535.)*

*The published state of this plate includes an aquatint ground, a title in the exergue (below the stage)* ΤꞶΝ ΜΕΝΤΟΙ ΧΗΝꞶΝ ΟΥΚ ΕΣΤΙΝ ΟΣΤΙΖ ΟΥ *(Nevertheless there is not a goose that cannot) and the following engraved inscription below the design: 'A Stranger at Sparta standing long upon one leg, said to a Lacedaemonian,/I do not believe you can do as much; "True (said he) but every Goose can". See Plutarch's Laconic Apothegms Vol. I. Page 406.'*

*Dance, the painter, was paid fifty guineas for the drawing for this design (now in the Fitzwilliam Museum, Cambridge), in which the hat and tunic are coloured light pink. Auguste Vestris called it a 'libellous falsehood', and was doubtless even more indignant at another version of the design in reverse with different details throughout, published on 6th May, 1781. This showed the young dancer with his right hand holding a hat full of notes inscribed £1100 and £2000 and his left hand holding a purse full of guineas, a bawdy comment serving as title (see No. 26415 in Print Room). The Vestris family were*

*Florentine in origin but had performed so long in Paris that popular resentment in England against the French during a war with France became focused on the enormous sums of money made by the brilliant and conceited pair during their visit to London.*

*The inscribed reference to Vauxhall cannot be confirmed. This was the name of a district on the South bank of London opened about 1660 as a pleasure garden in which public entertainments were given. It was closed in 1859.*

BARTOLOZZI, Francesco, R.A. (1727–1815), possibly after Nathaniel DANCE, R.A. (later Sir N. Dance-Holland, Bt.) (1734–1811).

**67** JASON ET MÉDÉE. BALLET TRAGIQUE. Lettered *Publishd July 3rd 1781 by John Boydell Engraver in Cheapside London.*

*Etching and aquatint in two shades of brown;* $16\frac{7}{16} \times 18\frac{3}{4}$       E.2836–1962
Purchased from the funds of the Enthoven Bequest.

*Gaëtan Vestris (1729–1808) is shown in this satirical print making what was expected to be his last appearance on 19th June, 1781, in the 1780–1781 London season, in his adaptation of Noverre's ballet* Jason and Medea. *Nevertheless he appeared finally on the London stage in that season on 26th June, 1781. His first appearance in this ballet was on 29th March, 1781, at the King's Theatre, Haymarket, London, where it was offered as his own invention. Although modified in later productions such as this, the choreography was actually invented by Jean Georges Noverre (1727–1809) in 1763, and the music played at the King's Theatre in 1781 was apparently from the original score of 1763 by Jean Joseph Rodolphe (1730–1812). The scenery for the 1781 production was by Novosielski, a stage designer working in London in the late eighteenth century.*

*This print is also interesting in that it shows in its satirical manner how a dramatic element had crept into the stylised ballet traditions of the seventeenth and eighteenth centuries. For that, Noverre, the original choreographer of* Jason and Medea, *was chiefly responsible. He and a French* corps de ballet *had been invited from Paris to London by David Garrick to perform at Drury Lane Theatre as far back as 1755, and it was the revelation of Garrick's acting which suggested to Noverre the idea of revitalising the ballet form by a more dramatic style of choreography. Thus he can be said to have originated the* ballet d'action. *Noverre was* maître de ballets en chef *at the* Opéra *in Paris from 1775 to 1780, and the author of the most famous of eighteenth-century theoretical works on the ballet,* Lettres sur la Danse et les Ballets, *first published at Lyons in 1760.*

*The 1780s were the last years in which men in the 'noble' or 'heroic' ballets danced in 'heroic' costumes with* tonnelets *and* tunics recalling ancient Roman loricas. *The clothes of Gaëtan Vestris as designed by Novosielski for the role of Jason should be compared with the costume shown in Plate 58. The rococo decoration of 1744 is seen to have given way to the Neo-Classical plainness of 1781, enriched by a single embroidered and jewelled star on the front of Gaëtan's tunic: the basques have become little tabs to which the cloak is attached on one side; the* tonnelet *is apparently cut into modified sectors and no longer stiffened. The dresses of the female dancers, on the other hand, are neither antiquarian nor especially theatrical.*

SANDBY, Paul, R.A. (1725–1809), attributed to.

**68** Two men, probably Gaëtan and Auguste Vestris, dancing in a ballet, *c.* 1780–1781.
*Ink and water-colour over pencil, size of sheet* $7\frac{5}{8}\times11\frac{3}{8}$         E.457–1955

   *Both Gaëtan Vestris (1728–1808) and his son Auguste (1760–1842) appeared for the first time in London in 1780, and their accomplishments as dancers caused a sensation. It is reasonable to assume they are represented here, although the representations are clearly satirical. The left-hand figure (? Gaëtan) is shown with a rose-coloured hat, tunic and shoes, and blue-green breeches: the colour-scheme of the other figure is in reverse, with rose-coloured breeches.*

   *On the back of the sheet are two sketches in pencil, pen and wash: one of a male dancer wearing a large hat, the other of a female dancer wearing a hooped skirt.*


BERTHET, Louis (worked late 18th century), after Louis BINET (1744–*c.* 1800).

**69** Ballet scene in Act 4 of the opera *Armide et Renaud*, composed by Lulli in 1686. It shows the dancers (left to right) Agate-Vogelein, Zénéide (centre), Telaire and Jasameth (right); and another in the role of Renaud seated on the left.

   Frontispiece to *Les Danseuses* in *Les Contemporaines graduées, ou Aventures des Jolies-Femmes de l'age actuel suivant la gradacion des principaux États de la Société*, by N. E. Restif de la Bretonne, Volume XLI, p. 114, Paris, 1785.
*Engraving; cut to* $7\times3\frac{7}{8}$         29533.19


BERTHET, Louis (worked late 18th century), after Louis BINET (1744–*c.* 1800).

**70** Ballet scene in the last *entrée* in the opera *Psyché*, composed by Lulli in 1678; showing the followers of Apollo, Bacchus, Momus and Mars.

   Frontispiece to *Les Figurantes* in *Les Contemporaines graduées* etc., by N. E. Restif de la Bretonne, Vol. XLII, p 149, Paris, 1785.
*Engraving; cut to* $6\frac{7}{8}\times3\frac{7}{8}$         29533.23

   *This print and the one above (Plate 69) illustrate typical feminine dress in heroic ballets during the reign of Louis XVI, and almost certainly depict costumes based on designs by Louis René Boquet, dessinateur en chef des habits du Roi pour fêtes, spectacles et cérémonies from 1764 to 1792, and designer-in-chief at the Opéra, Paris, from 1759 until the Revolution. Whereas Plate 62 shows Boquet's earlier Rococo manner, these prints give some idea of the style of his later inventions dating from c. 1760 to c. 1792, in which ornamental garlands are as conspicuous as in the decorations of Louis Seize architecture and furniture.*


CONDÉ, Jean (died 1794), after H. de JANVRY (working 1794–1800).

**71** Mademoiselle Hilligsberg in the ballet *Le Jaloux Puni*, 1794. Proof before letters.
*Stipple engraving;* $11\frac{3}{4}\times9\frac{1}{16}$         Enthoven Collection

   Le Jaloux Puni, *by James d'Egville (working 1783–1827), was first produced at the King's Theatre, London, on 1st June, 1793.*

   *The appearance of women in male roles is still frequent in pantomimes and seems to have become popular during the eighteenth century. On 15th April, 1779, for example, The Public Advertiser announced that a military pantomime-ballet called* La Bravoure des Femmes *would be performed at the King's Theatre, 'in which Madame Simonet in the Character of Leading Officer [would] fight a Duel at Small Sword'.*

PIROLI, Tommaso (1752–1824), after Friedrich REHBERG (1758–1835).

**72** Dancing. The sixth Attitude from *Lady Hamilton's Attitudes*, Part I; a book of twelve plates by Piroli from Rehberg's drawings of Emma, Lady Hamilton, made at Naples in 1794. Published by S. W. Forbes, 50 Piccadilly, London, 1797.

*Engraving on terra-cotta paper;* $10\frac{1}{8} \times 8$            E.5763–1905

*Emma Lyon (c. 1765–1815), afterwards Lady Hamilton, and well known as the mistress of Nelson, became the wife of Sir William Hamilton, British Envoy Extraordinary at Naples, in 1791. This man played a certain part in shaping the Neo-Classic taste of the end of the eighteenth century, and was probably his wife's mentor in the striking of her once famous attitudes.*

*The attitudes, or mimes, were based upon the postures of figures in Antique gems and sculptures. In his* Italienische Reise, *Goethe records spending two happy evenings at Naples in 1787, watching Emma Hamilton bring to life—so he felt—the female figures in Greek and Roman works of art. She was, in fact, a Neo-Classic mime, or poseuse, and though her performances were entirely domestic, they had a little of the same value as stimuli to artists as the eurhythmics of Isidora Duncan a century later.*

ANONYMOUS, after Aloys Ludwig HIRT (1759–1837).

**73, 74** Plates from a series of twelve designs attributable to Hirt for *Dädalus und Seine Statuen, ein Pantomimischer Tanz*, Berlin, 1802.

*Etchings, coloured by hand*

**73** Theseus and Antiope.
$6\frac{1}{4} \times 6\frac{5}{8}$            Library

**74** Cephalus and Aurora.
$6\frac{3}{8} \times 6\frac{7}{8}$            Library

*The book,* Dädalus und Seine Statuen, *which was edited by Hirt, describes an entertainment combining pantomime and dance, performed on 23rd March, 1802, in the palace of Prince Ferdinand of Prussia, various members of the court taking part. The music was by Vincenzo Righini (1756–1812), who succeeded Alessandri at the Italian opera school at Berlin. The production of the pantomime and dance was undertaken by Telle.*

*In the text reference is made to* Lady Hamilton's Attitudes *as one source of inspiration for the mimes.*

ANONYMOUS (English, *c.* 1805).

**75** Title of the score for a musical accompaniment to *Crazy Jane*, first performed for Monsieur and Madame Laborie's benefit at the King's Theatre, London, on 4th April, 1805.

*Engraving;* $10\frac{3}{4} \times 7\frac{7}{8}$            Enthoven Collection

*Laborie and his wife, who both danced in this production, did not return to the stage afterwards. The music, arranged in this case for piano and harp, was by Federigo Fiorillo (1753–1823 or after), in London from 1788 to 1794; and by Michael Kelly (1762–1826), a composer and tenor singer, for a time acting manager of the King's Theatre. The choreography was by James d'Egville (working 1783–1827), son of the Frenchman Peter Dagville or Daigueville, who had been ballet-master at Drury Lane and at Sadler's Wells in the second half of the eighteenth century.*

*James d'Egville's first ballet seems to have been Le Jaloux Puni produced in 1793 at the King's Theatre (see Plate 71), where he became ballet-master from 1799 to 1809, three seasons excepted. He kept a dancing school during the period of the Napoleonic Wars at a time when it was hard to get dancers from abroad, thus providing a nursery and a standard for English ballet.*

*The themes of d'Egville's ballets were often English, but English taste, and certain vested interests, did not permit him to lay any firm foundations for an English school of ballet, though he might otherwise have achieved this. The general public had already made it clear by 1809 that it preferred foreign talent at all costs, and with the close of the Napoleonic Wars most of the important roles were taken once again by dancers of continental repute.*

*Captain Rees Gronow in his Recollections and Anecdotes (new ed. 1877, pp. 35–36) remembered that 'When George the Fourth was Regent, her Majesty's Theatre [formerly the King's Theatre], as the Italian Opera in the Haymarket is still called, was conducted on a very different system from that which now prevails. Some years previous to the period to which I refer, no one could obtain a box or a ticket for the pit without a voucher from one of the lady patronesses, who, in 1815 were the Duchesses of Marlborough, Devonshire, and Bedford, Lady Carlisle, and some others. In their day, after the singing and the ballet were over, the company used to retire into the concert-room, where a ball took place, accompanied by refreshments and a supper. There all the rank and fashion of England were assembled on a sort of neutral ground.*

*'At a later period, the management of the Opera House fell into the hands of Mr. Waters, when it became less difficult to obtain admittance; but the strictest etiquette was still kept up as regarded the dress of the gentlemen, who were only admitted with knee-buckles, ruffles and* chapeau bras. *If there happened to be a drawing-room, the ladies would appear in their court-dresses, as well as the gentlemen.'*

JOLY, Adrien Jean Baptiste (Muffat) (1772–1839).

**76** Beaupré as Paul in the ballet *Paul et Virginie* at the *Opéra, Paris, c.* 1806. No. 76 in Hautecoeur Martinet's *Galerie Théâtrale*, Paris, 1820.

*Etching, coloured by hand;* $7\frac{15}{16} \times 4\frac{3}{4}$                    Library

*Joly was an actor as well as a draughtsman. Based on Bernardin de St. Pierre's famous story, this ballet was written by Pierre Gabriel Gardel (1758–1840) and first produced at the Paris* Opéra *on 25th June, 1806.*

*The costume is meant to resemble the sort of clothes that would have been seen in Mauritius in the eighteenth century. Striped trousers were much worn in tropical colonies and by sailors, though it is unlikely that they were ever quite so short as they are shown here. In fact, this is an early representation of 'shorts', possibly intended to give the dancer a juvenile appearance as well as allowing him more freedom of action. The 'shorts' are yellow with red stripes; the sash purple; the shoes red.*

BAQUOY, Pierre Charles (1759–1829), after Silvestre David MIRYS (1742–1810).

**77** O CHUTE ÉPOUVANTABLE ET DIGNE DE MÉMOIRE! Frontispiece engraved by Baquoy after a design by Mirys for *La Danse, ou la Guerre des Dieux de l'Opéra,* an epic poem by Joseph Berchoux (1765–1839) on the rivalry between the dancers Duport and Auguste Vestris (1760–1842). From the second edition, Paris, 1808.

*Engraving;* $6 \times 3\frac{5}{8}$                    Library: Piot Collection 608

*The composition shows Vestris II in the role of Ulysses, having collapsed after attempting one* entrechat *too many; while Duport, as Ajax, continues to dance. The event is purely fictitious, and no ballet based on the subject existed. In Berchoux's poem it symbolised the rise of Duport and the decline in fame of Vestris II during the early years of the nineteenth century—though in fact this can hardly be said to have taken place.*

*It is interesting to note how the Neo-Classical movement in the arts during the late eighteenth century had by this time affected the style of costumes worn in Grecian roles. These costumes make some pretence to antiquarian accuracy.*

BIASIOLI, Angelo (1790–1830), after Alessandro SANQUIRICO (1780–1849).

**78** LUOGO INTERNO NEL QUARTIERE DEGLI STRELITZI. NOTTE. Scene in Act V of the heroic ballet *I Strelitzi*, as performed at the Scala Theatre, Milan, on 26 December, 1811. From *Raccolta di Varie Decorazioni Sceniche inventate e dipinte dal Pittore Alessandro Sanquirico per L'I. R. Teatro alla Scala in Milano* [c. 1827].
*Etching and aquatint, coloured by hand;* $13\frac{1}{8} \times 15\frac{3}{4}$ E.3209–1915

*The engraved title of the print says that this scene is in Act IV of the ballet, but the scenery corresponds with that of Act V as described by Cyril Beaumont in his* Complete Book of Ballets, *p. 35.*

I Strelitzi *means 'The Archers', which in Russia at this date was the name used sometimes for the standing army. The story and choreography of the ballet was by Salvatore Viganò (1769–1821), maître de ballet at the Scala Theatre from 1812 until his death. In this work he gave substance for the first time in his career to his notion of a coherent dance drama, involving a much closer correlation of music and movement than had been sought in the eighteenth century, when ballets were frequently no more than serial alternations of miming and formal dances. It was composed in 1809, after* Ippotoo, *and first performed at La Fenice Theatre, Venice, in that year. The music was adapted to the requirements of the ballet from already-written pieces by contemporary composers.*

*The story of* I Strelitzi *hinges upon a plot against the Russian crown and is an early example of the use of, and the realistic presentation of, a Russian theme. During the Napoleonic wars Europe became more conscious of Russia then ever before, and the ballets* Pietro il Grande, *by Rossi, and* Katchell, *by Didelot, are further evidence of increasing interest in that country.*

LOSE, Carolina (worked early 19th century), after Alessandro SANQUIRICO (1780–1849).

**79** RUPIE SCOSCESI SCOGLI CHE SI ESTENDONO SINO AL MARE FORMANDO UNA RADA CAPACE DI VARI GROSSI VASCELLI etc. Scene at the entrance of a cave by the sea-shore in the tragic ballet *L'Alunno della Giumenta ossia l'Ippotoo Vendicato* (The Harlot's Pupil or Ippotoo Revenged), as performed at the Scala Theatre, Milan, on 13 June, 1812. From *Raccolta di Varie Decorazioni Sceniche inventate e dipinte dal Pittore Alessandro Sanquirico per L'I. R. Teatro alla Scala in Milano* [c. 1827].
*Etching and aquatint, coloured by hand;* $13\frac{3}{16} \times 15\frac{7}{8}$ E.3206–1915

*The choreography of* Ippotoo *was composed by Salvatore Viganò (1769–1821) at Padua in 1809, and the ballet was first performed in that city. The scene designed by Sanquirico, presumably for the Scala production, might be said to be in the English Romantic manner, and, strangely enough, there is in the Museum a similar cave-scene with inverted lighting designed by Philip James De Loutherbourg between 1771 and 1785 for the theatres at Drury Lane and Covent Garden (E.159–1937).*

*The music of Viganò's ballets was generally by various composers: when nothing suitable could be thought of he supplied musical inventions of his own.*

CASARTELLI (working first half of 19th century).

**80** The three kinds of ballet, showing typical costumes. Plate XIV, engraved by Casartelli from his own design, in *Traité . . . de l'Art de la Danse*, by Carlo Blasis, Milan, 1820.

*Etching;* $8\frac{1}{4} \times 9\frac{15}{16}$     Library: Piot Collection 969

*This is an extremely useful print, because it illustrates the classification of ballet dancing just after the* Empire, *according to the most famous of the nineteenth-century teachers and theorists of the ballet*

*In the upper row of Figures, No. 1 represents a pair of* Danseurs Serieux, *in the noble tradition, wearing 'Greek' costumes: No. 2 shows a pair in the* demi-caractère *style, wearing Spanish troubadour costumes; and No. 3, two dancers in the comic or* villageois *style, wearing pastoral costumes. It will be noted that all these costumes have a pronounced* Empire *look, whether they derive from Neo-Classical antiquarianism (No. 1), or from the evening dress of the period (No. 3).*

*The lower row shows the principal group in a Bacchanale invented by Blasis himself.*

*Carlo Blasis (1803–1878) was a noted writer on ballet, whose best-known work* The Code of Terpsichore, *appeared in English in 1830. In 1837 he became director of the Imperial Academy at Milan, and his training radiated from there to all parts of the world, including Russia.*

STUCCHI, Stanislao (worked early 19th century) and LANDINI, (?) Domenico (worked early 19th century), after Alessandro SANQUIRICO (1780–1849).

**81** PADIGLIONE. Scene inside a pavilion in the tragic ballet *La Presa di Babilonia* (The Capture of Babylon), as performed at the Scala Theatre, Milan, on 23 April, 1821. From *Raccolta di Scene Teatrali esguito o disegnate dai piu celebri Pittori Scenici in Milano, Parte I*, Milan, *c.* 1823.

*Etching and aquatint;* $6 \times 7\frac{5}{16}$     E.387–1930

*The sub-title of another print in the Museum (E.3223–1915) showing a different scene in this ballet tells us that the choreography was by Francesco Clerico.*

*In its regular repetition of form, Sanquirico's design appears very Neo-Classical, and the only details that might be said to evoke Babylon are the curious capitals and bases of the columns, reminiscent of the Persic Pillars in English Regency furniture and conceived in a similar train of thought, no doubt. In accordance with Sanquirico's general practice, the spacing, which reveals only part of the pavilion, is contrived to give the effect of an almost overwhelming magnificence of scale.*

STUCCHI, Stanislao (worked early 19th century) and LANDINI, (?) Domenico (worked early 19th century), after Alessandro SANQUIRICO (1780–1849).

**82** SALA CHE METTE AL GIARDINO. Scene of a room opening on a garden in the ballet *Alfredo il Grande* (Alfred the Great), as performed at the Scala Theatre, Milan, on 12 February, 1822. From *Raccolta di Scene Teatrali esguito o disegnate dai piu celebri Pittori Scenici in Milano, Parte I*, Milan, *c.* 1823.

*Etching and aquatint;* $6\frac{1}{4} \times 7\frac{1}{2}$     E.422–1930

*The choreography of the ballet was by Jean Aumer (1776–1833), and the music by Count von Gallenberg (1783–1839) and Gustave Dugazon (1782–1826). It was first performed in Vienna in 1820.*

*This Neo-Romanesque scene, with its enormous arch full of stained glass as in a Victorian conservatory, was meant to suggest the environment of an English Saxon monarch in the ninth century. Further touches of Romantic anachronism are the Classical statuary in the garden, the wall-painting of a battle scene, and the flowers in Neo-Classical vases on three-legged monopodium tables. The theatrical effect is however powerful.*

*Alfred the Great was performed later at the King's Theatre, London, on 8th March, 1823; at which theatre Aumer was maître de ballet from 1823 until 1825.*

BOULLAY (working early 19th century), after Charles CHARLES (working 1820–1845).

**83** Pierson in the ballet *Suzanne* by Blache at the *Théâtre de la Porte St. Martin*, Paris, c. 1820. No. 445 in Hautecoeur Martinet's *Galerie Théâtrale*, Paris, 1820.

*Etching, coloured by hand;* $7\frac{9}{16} \times 4\frac{5}{8}$                          Library

*The costume of this Biblical character, presumably an elder, is interesting in that it is still partly Graeco-Roman in the Baroque style. The cloak is coloured brown and the undergarment gray.*

*According to the lettering at the base of the print the pose of the dancer occurs in Scene I of Act I of* Suzanne, *a ballet no longer readily traceable. Some of the performances at theatres of the second rank were of ballets, vaudevilles and plays which never appeared at institutions like the* Opéra, *and did not survive in the memories of the public, or in later repertories.*

CHARLES, Charles (working c. 1820–1845).

**84** Pierson and Madame Pierson in the roles of Fritz and Cécilia in the ballet-pantomime *La Fille Soldat* by the two Blaches (father and son in collaboration) at the *Théâtre de la Porte St. Martin*, Paris, c. 1820. No. 464 in Hautecoeur Martinet's *Galerie Théâtrale*, Paris, 1820.

*Etching, coloured by hand;* $7\frac{1}{2} \times 5\frac{1}{16}$                          Library

*The male costume here is* ancien régime *in character, with the exception of the bicorne hat which is in the 1800 style. On the other hand, the female costume is inconsistently* Empire *in outline.*

*Jean Baptiste Blache was* maître de ballet *at the* Théâtre de la Porte St. Martin *during the* Empire *and* Restauration *periods. He was assisted for a time by his son, François Alexis Blache, who went to St. Petersburg in 1838. It is possible that this ballet may have been based upon one by d'Egville called* Heliska, ou La Fille Soldat, *produced on 29th December, 1801, at the King's Theatre, London: or both ballets may have been based upon an older unidentified one having a similar subject.*

ANONYMOUS, after Auguste Simon GARNEREY (1785–1824).

**85 – 88** Illustrations (4) of costumes in the ballet-pantomime *Clari* as performed at the *Opéra*, Paris, c. 1820. From the series *Recueil des costumes de tous les ouvrages dramatiques représentés avec succès sur les grands théâtres de Paris*, published by Vizentini, *comedien du Roi*, Paris, 1819–1822.

*Lithographs, coloured by hand*

**85** Monsieur Albert as the Duke Mevilla.
$7\frac{7}{8} \times 4\frac{7}{8}$                          Library

**86** Monsieur Ferdinand as a valet of the Duke Mevilla.
$8 \times 4\frac{7}{8}$                                                                 Library

**87** Madame Élie as a companion of the Duke Mevilla.
$8\frac{1}{2} \times 4\frac{7}{8}$                                                       Library

**88** Mademoiselle Brocard as a young comedienne.
$8\frac{7}{8} \times 4\frac{7}{8}$                                                       Library

*Garnerey was chief costume designer at the* Opéra *from 1819 to 1824, and also for the* Théâtre Français. *His designs were in the Romantic genre troubadour. The ballet* Clari *in three acts with music by Rodolphe Kreutzer (1766–1831) and choreography by Louis Milon (1765–1849), was first presented at the* Opéra *in 1820.*

*Ferdinand Albert Decombe, known as Albert, lived from 1789 to 1865, and became one of the best-known male dancers of the* Restauration *period. Here his costume is meant to be sixteenth century in character, but the hat suggests a much earlier date in that century than the doublet and hose. Other inconsistencies appear in the costume of the valet; while in those of the two women almost no effort has been made towards antiquarian suitability.*

ANONYMOUS, after Auguste Simon GARNEREY (1785–1824).

**89** A young Ephesian scattering flowers in a ballet in the third act of the tragedy *Olimpie*, as performed at the *Opéra*, Paris, c. 1820. From the series *Recueil des costumes de tous les ouvrages dramatiques représentés avec succès sur les grands théâtres de Paris*, published by Vizentini, *comedien du Roi*, Paris, 1819–1822.
*Lithograph, coloured by hand;* $8\frac{3}{16} \times 5\frac{1}{4}$                      Library

*This costume appears to have consisted mainly of transparent white muslin, the rest being light blue.*

*Sosthène de la Rochefoucauld, superintendant of the* Opéra *in the period of the Bourbon Restoration, regulated that the skirts of dancers should be lengthened by one third. In his story, A Prince of Bohemia.* Balzac *remarks that these and other prudish reforms of the 1820s ruined the ballet in* Paris *during those years.*

ANONYMOUS, after Auguste Simon GARNEREY (1785–1824).

**90** Illustration of the costume worn by Milon as the Comte de Murer in the ballet *Les Pages du duc de Vendôme* at the *Opéra*, Paris, c. 1820. From the series *Recueil des costumes de tous les ouvrages dramatiques représentés avec succès sur les grands théâtres de Paris*, published by Vizentini, *comedien du Roi*, Paris, 1819–1822.
*Lithograph, coloured by hand;* $8\frac{9}{16} \times 5$                               Library

*The choreography and story of this ballet in a single act were by Jean Aumer (1776–1833), and the score by Adalbert Gyrowetz (?1763–1850). It was first performed in Vienna at the Kaernthner Thor Theatre on 16th October, 1815, and at the* Opéra, *Paris, on 8th October, 1820.*

*Louis Milon (1765–1849) was the choreographer of* Clari *and ballet-master at the* Opéra. *Garnerey's design here represents a pioneering effort in the re-creation of historic costume. At this period the antiquarian sense was developing alongside a Romantic interest in the past. But the beard and hair-style are too early for the clothes, and the tricorne hat is unconvincing.*

FAUCONNIER (worked first half of 19th century), after Hippolyte LECOMTE (1781–1857).

91, 92 Illustrations (2) of costumes in the dance in the opera *Pharamond*, as performed at the *Opéra*, Paris, *c.* 1820. From the series *Recueil des costumes de tous les ouvrages dramatiques représentés avec succès sur les grands théâtres de Paris*, published by Vizentini, *comedien du Roi*, Paris, 1819–1822.

*Lithographs, coloured by hand*

91 Young Gaulish woman. Costume worn by Mademoiselles Brocard and Vigneron, and others.
$8\frac{5}{8} \times 5$                                                                                     Library

92 Frankish warrior. Costume worn by Monsieur Gosselin and others.
$8\frac{1}{2} \times 4\frac{7}{8}$                                                                         Library

*Lecomte rose to occupy the position of chief costume designer at the* Opéra *from 1824 to 1830, when he was succeeded by Eugène Lami. His designs were of the* genre troubadour, *in which Garnerey practised.*


STÜRMER, Heinrich (?1774–1855), after Wilhelm HENSEL (1794–1861).

93, 94 Plates (2) from *Lalla Rûkh, Ein Festspiel mit Gesang und Tanz*, Berlin, 1822; a literary and pictorial record of the entertainment given on 27th January, 1821, at the Royal Palace, Berlin, in honour of the visit of the Grand Duke Nicholas and Grand Duchess Alexandra Feodorovna of Russia.

*Etchings, coloured by hand*

93 Bucharian dancers.
$8\frac{5}{16} \times 6\frac{7}{8}$                                                                       Library

94 Indian dancers.
$7\frac{15}{16} \times 7\frac{1}{4}$                                                                      Library

*The entertainment, performed by the Grand Duke Nicholas and the Grand Duchess Alexandra Feodorovna of Russia and members of the Prussian court, included scenes and songs based on passages in Thomas Moore's poem* Lalla Rookh, *interspersed with dances. Karl Friedrich Schinkel, an architect working in the Prussian version of the Biedermeier style, was responsible for the decorations and the grouping of the performers. The costumes were designed by Wilhelm Hensel who, for his Indian subjects, referred to painted illustrations in an Indian book in the Prussian Royal Library.*


WALDECK, F. (worked early 19th century).

95 Mons^r. Albert, from the Academy of Music, Paris. In the Character of Alcides: King's Theatre. Published by H. Berthoud, London, 1821.
*Lithograph;* $8\frac{5}{8} \times 5\frac{5}{8}$                                          Enthoven Collection

*The ballet* Alcide, *with choreography by Ferdinand Albert (1789–1865) and Deshayes, was produced at the King's Theatre, London, on 21st July, 1821.*

*Albert's costume is decorated in a late Neo-Classical style, and is in the noble tradition for a Greek tragic subject.*

CASTELLINI, L. (worked early 19th century), after Alessandro SANQUIRICO (1780–1849).

96  INTERNO DEL PALAZZO DI CLEOPATRA. Scene I in Act III of the historical ballet *Cleopatra in Tarso*, as performed at the Scala Theatre, Milan, on 26 December, 1821. From *Raccolta di Varie Decorazione Sceniche inventate e dipinte dal Pittore Alessandro Sanquirico per L'I. R. Teatro alla Scala in Milano* [c. 1827].

*Etching and aquatint, coloured by hand; 13×15⅜*                    E.3197–1915

In this scene, outside Cleopatra's palace, the queen is about to refresh herself with fruit brought to her by a peasant after Anthony has been borne away to die by Octavia and her sons. The ballet, composed by Jean Aumer (1776–1833) with music by Rodolphe Kreutzer (1766–1831), was first performed in 1807 at Lyons where Aumer was for a time maître de ballet. In the following year it appeared at the Opéra in Paris, and was later performed frequently at Cassel and at Vienna where Aumer became successively maître de ballet.

Egyptian motifs were very popular in decorative art in the late eighteenth and early nineteenth centuries, and after Napoleon's campaign in North Africa historical curiosity about ancient Egypt increased. Sanquirico seems to have made numerous re-creations of Egyptian interiors for the Scala stage, too nearly accurate perhaps to come under the heading of pastiche and yet successfully retaining the portentous tomb-like qualities so admired by Romantics.

CASTELLINI, L. (worked early 19th century), after Alessandro SANQUIRICO (1780–1849).

97  TEMPIO DI MECCA. Scene in a mosque in Mecca in the tragic ballet *Maometto*, as performed at the Scala Theatre, Milan, on 11 June, 1822. From *Raccolta di Varie Decorazione Sceniche inventate e dipinte dal Pittore Alessandro Sanquirico per L'I. R. Teatro alla Scala in Milano* [c. 1827].

*Etching and aquatint, coloured by hand; 12¹⁵⁄₁₆×15⁵⁄₁₆*                    E.3225–1915

This ballet, based on the story of Mahomet, was the invention—so the engraved title records—of Francesco Clerico. Sanquirico's design for the inside of a mosque is interesting in that it shows how the exotic in this period could be (and often was) offered in terms of the familiar. Thus the symmetrical view is Baroque in the style of the Bibieni; but the clustered columns are Gothic. The statue on the pedestal is Neo-Classical and quite out of place in any mosque; while the Saracen arches are decorated with Greek palmettes, and the hanging lamps are in an early nineteenth-century style. The total design seems all the more romantic and mysterious by reason of these historical discrepancies.

COOPER, Robert (worked 1795–1836), after F. WALDECK (worked early 19th century).

98  Monr. Le Blond; at the King's Theatre, London. Published by H. Berthoud, Junior, 19th July, 1822.

*Stipple engraving, coloured by hand; 10½×8*                    Enthoven Collection

It is not certain what ballet Le Blond is supposed to be represented in; but it may be Pandore, with choreography by Anatole and music by Jean Schneitzhoeffer (1787–1852), first performed at the King's Theatre on 12th January, 1822. The waistcoat is coloured yellow-brown, and the tie and edges of the breech-strings, blue. The costume is in the comic or villageois style, and is in almost every respect similar to the text-book version in Fig. 3 of Plate 80.

*Within a few years of this date the status of the male dancer began to decline, while attention became more and more concentrated on the ballerina.*

ANONYMOUS (French, *c.* 1823).

**99** Mademoiselle Bigotini and Ferdinand Albert, in the role of Prince Ramir, in the ballet *Cendrillon*, produced at the *Opéra*, Paris, in 1823.

*Etching and engraving, coloured by hand; cut to $5\frac{7}{16} \times 4\frac{13}{16}$*     E.2437–1930
Given by Miss D. Stern.

*The music of this ballet was by Ferdinand Sor (1780–1829), composer for the guitar, and the choreography by Ferdinand Albert (1789–1865).*

*As so often before in the eighteenth and seventeenth centuries, the woman's costume differs very little in its shape and embroidery from women's ordinary clothes of the time, except in this case for the pseudo-Renaissance hat. A similar hat is worn by the male partner, whose skirted tunic maintains one of the traditions of the eighteenth century, while the hose and leg-of-mutton sleeves give the early Renaissance echoes.*

Cendrillon *was a ballet in* demi-caractère.

LOSE, Carolina (worked early 19th century), after Alessandro SANQUIRICO (1780–1849).

**100** ESTERNO DI UNA CAPANNA. Scene outside a hut in the ballet-pantomime *Il Naufragio di La Peyrouse*, as performed at the *Teatro alla Canobbiana* in the autumn of 1825. From *Raccolta di Varie Decorazione Sceniche inventate e dipinte dal Pittore Alessandro Sanquirico per L'I. R. Teatro alla Scala in Milano [c. 1827].*

*Etching and aquatint, coloured by hand; $13 \times 14\frac{1}{2}$*     E.3200–1915

*According to the engraved title, this ballet was composed by William Barrymore, presumably the Irish actor of that name known to have lived and worked for many years on the continent in the first quarter of the nineteenth century. The interest of the Romantic design lies chiefly in the forms of the realistic palm trees grouped asymmetrically on the left and of a size in relation to the rest of the landscape almost inconceivable in the eighteenth century, when they would have been given less emphasis.*

*La Peyrouse was the explorer (1741–1788) more properly called Count de La Pérouse, after whom was named the Strait of Pérouse discovered by him in 1787. In the following year he was shipwrecked and died off the island of Vanikoro.*

LOSE, Carolina (worked early 19th century), after Alessandro SANQUIRICO (1780–1849).

**101** INTERNO DI UNA SERRA. Conservatory scene in the character-ballet *Elerz e Zulmida*, as performed at the Scala Theatre, Milan, on 6 May, 1826. From *Raccolta di Varie Decorazione Sceniche inventate e dipinte dal Pittore Alessandro Sanquirico per L'I. R. Teatro alla Scala in Milano [c. 1827].*

*Etching and aquatint, coloured by hand; $13\frac{1}{8} \times 15\frac{7}{16}$*     E.3173–1915

*This ballet was invented by Luigi Henry, with music by Cesare Pugni.*

*Sanquirico's design is of interest, apart from the beautiful articulation of its details, in that it depicts convincingly and without undue fantasy one of the glass conservatories then being built all over Europe. This one seems to be intended to be of wood construction, although in England cast iron was used soon after at Syon House, for example, on a large*

101. CAROLINA LOSE, after A. Sanquirico. Scene in *Elerz e Zulmida*, 1826. Coloured etching and aquatint, *c.* 1827.

*scale. A more descriptive representation of the exotic plants coming into fashion at this date would be hard to find.*

*The costumes of the figures consist of contemporary Central European (?Austrian) uniforms for the men, and walking clothes for the women.*

CHALON, Alfred Edward, R.A. (1780–1860).

**102** Caricature of Mademoiselle Brocard as Venus and Mélanie Duval as L'Amour in D'Egville's ballet *La Naissance de Venus* at the King's Theatre, London, 8th April, 1826. Dated 1826.

*Water-colour and pen and ink;* $13 \times 17\frac{3}{4}$            E.946–1924

*James D'Egville (working 1783–1827) had been ballet-master at the King's Theatre as far back as the first decade of the century, and returned in that capacity in 1826 and 1827. La Naissance de Venus has been considered his most successful ballet (see Ivor Guest,* The Romantic Ballet in England, *London, 1954, p. 36). The music was by Robert N. C. Bochsa (1789–1856), an eminent harpist and composer who left France in 1817 to escape being imprisoned for forgery, and settled in London where he succeeded Carlo Coccia (1782–1873) as conductor at the King's Theatre from 1826–1832.*

*This drawing, and the next two, belong to a series of caricatures of actors and singers made by Chalon, presumably on the spot, during the 1820s and 1830s. Very little got past his sense of the ridiculous; which does not prevent the drawing of Mlle Brocard in particular from being of high quality.*

CHALON, Alfred Edward, R.A. (1780–1860).

**103** Caricature of Louis François Gosselin in the ballet *Le Carnaval de Venise* at the King's Theatre, London, *c.* 1830.

*Water-colour;* $14\frac{1}{4} \times 7\frac{3}{8}$            E.3324–1922

*The drawing is inscribed by Chalon 'Goslin Carnaval de Venise ou tout ce que vous voudrez. 1830. Il est, il est, il est toujours le même.'*

*This ballet was first produced at the Opéra, Paris, in 1816 by Louis Milon (1765–1849), assistant maître de ballet to Pierre Gardel. It was produced at the King's Theatre first on 31st May, 1821, and again in 1822, 1823 and 1830.*

*From 1842 until 1852 Gosselin was a sous-maître de ballet under Benjamin Lumley, the celebrated manager of Her Majesty's Theatre (the old King's Theatre) during the period of the later Romantic ballet in London. His cloak is shown as violet with gold embroidery, the tunic white, also embroidered along the hem with gold, and the hat black with white plumes.*

CHALON, Alfred Edward, R.A. (1780–1860).

**104** Caricature of Zoé Beaupré as Queen Elizabeth in the ballet *Kenilworth*, first produced on the 3rd March, 1831, at the King's Theatre, London, *c.* 1831.

*Water-colour;* $10\frac{7}{8} \times 8$            E.980–1924

*William Grieve (1800–1844) designed the sets for this ballet; Deshayes was the choreographer of it; and Michael Costa (1808–1884) the composer of the music for it.*

*The Queen's skirt is shown here as yellow, the bodice red and yellow, and the cloak, which is ermine-lined, appears to be of red and yellow damask. The stockings are red. The other costumes in the ballet were fairly accurate for their date, and the plot adhered closely to Sir Walter Scott's tale. A Pyrrhic dance and a masque in the early seventeenth-century English style were introduced.*

CHALON, Alfred Edward, R.A. (1780–1860).

**105** Marie Taglioni as Zoloé in the ballet *Le Dieu et la Bayadère* by Filippo Taglioni. From the series *Six des principaux rôles de Mlle Taglioni à Paris*, printed by Lemercier and published in 1831 by Rittner et Goupil, Boulevard Montmartre, No. 15, Paris.

*Lithograph;* $7\frac{11}{16} \times 4\frac{1}{2}$                    Enthoven Collection

*In this role Marie Taglioni (?1809–1884) made her name in Paris in 1830. The ballet, with music by Daniel Auber (1782–1871), was first produced at the* Opéra, Paris, *on 13th October, 1830. In London it appeared first with this dancer in the same role at the King's Theatre, 14th June, 1831.*

*The widely spaced embroidered motifs, still faintly* Empire *in character, and the heavy jewellery, are typical of costume fashions of the period. The skirt, of course, is shorter than would have been worn by anybody other than a dancer on the stage.*

*Copies of the set of six lithographs in which this print was issued were included in the series* Celebrated Opera Dancers of Her Majesty's Theatre, London, *c. 1846.*

CHALON, Alfred Edward, R.A. (1780–1860).

**106** Marie Taglioni as Flore in Didelot's ballet *Flore et Zéphire*. From the series *Six des principaux rôles de Mlle Taglioni à Paris*, printed by Lemercier and published in 1831 by Rittner et Goupil, Boulevard Montmartre, No. 15, Paris.

*Lithograph;* $7\frac{11}{16} \times 4\frac{1}{2}$                    Enthoven Collection

*Marie Taglioni (?1809–1884), who was generally considered the most gifted ballerina of the Romantic period, first appeared before an English audience in a revised version of* Flore et Zéphire *at the King's Theatre, London, on 3rd June, 1830. There is a lithograph by R. J. Lane (1800–1872) after a drawing by A. E. Chalon which shows her as she performed in London wearing the same costume (see C. W. Beaumont and S. Sitwell,* The Romantic Ballet, *plate 2). Copies of the set of six lithographs in which this print was issued were included in the series* Celebrated Opera Dancers of Her Majesty's Theatre, London, *c. 1845.*

*The first version of* Flore et Zéphire *was first produced in London by Charles Didelot (1767–1836) in 1796.*

LEVASSEUR (worked second quarter of 19th century).

**107**
**108** Signor Samingo (*sic*) and Mad<sup>e.</sup> Brugnoli in the Grand Ballet *L'Anneau Magique*. Sketches in the King's Theatre, Nos. 1 and 2; from a series of six plates published by R. Ackermann, 96 Strand, London, May, 1832. Printed by Meifred Lemercier & Co., 24 Leicester Square.

*Lithographs, coloured by hand; average size of sheets* $13\frac{5}{8} \times 10\frac{1}{8}$         E.752,753–1945
Given by Mr G. H. Clarke.

*Paolo Samengo and Amalia Brugnoli are shown in troubadour costumes in the* demi-caractère *style. In the case of Brugnoli the costume is more or less contemporary in design, the leg-of-mutton sleeves being fashionable in 1832. Samengo's clothes, on the other hand, have various features intended to give a Renaissance effect.*

110. Alfred Edward Chalon. Marie Taglioni in *La Sylphide*, 1832. Coloured lithograph, *c.* 1846.

*This is an early illustration of dancing on* pointes, *which came into vogue in London in 1829, though practised by Madame Brugnoli as far back as 1822, and evolved as a result of the disappearance of eighteenth-century heels, certainly by 1821 and probably some years before then.*

*The ballet was first performed at the King's Theatre on 31st March, 1832, with choreography by Ferdinand Albert (1789–1865) and music by the Count von Gallenberg (1783–1839).*

MALEUVRE, P. (working second quarter of 19th century).

**109** Lise Noblet as Effie in the ballet *La Sylphide*, as first presented at the *Opéra*, Paris, on 12th March, 1832. Published by Hautecoeur Martinet, Paris, *c.* 1832.

*Etching, coloured by hand; cut to* $6\frac{7}{8} \times 3\frac{7}{8}$          29947.6

*The costumes of the ballet were designed by Eugène Lami (1800–1890), and were among the various innovations which combined to distinguish the Romantic ballets from ballets of the* Empire *and* Restauration *periods. Marie Taglioni's costume, as* La Sylphide, *was decidedly novel (see Plate 110). Madame Noblet's, on the other hand, was close to the ordinary day-clothes of the time, with a shorter skirt. The plaid appears in this skirt because the locale of the ballet was Scotland. The story of* La Sylphide *was derived from Charles Nodier's tale* Trilby ou le Lutin d'Argail *(1822), itself inspired by the continental vogue for Sir Walter Scott's romances.*

CHALON, Alfred Edward, R.A. (1780–1860).

**110** Marie Taglioni as *La Sylphide* in the ballet of that name. One of the series *Celebrated Opera Dancers of Her Majesty's Theatre*, after drawings by various artists, published by Thomas McLean, London, *c.* 1846.

*Lithograph, coloured by hand; cut to* $16\frac{1}{2} \times 11\frac{3}{8}$          E.2885-1948

*The story of* La Sylphide *was an adaptation by Adolphe Nourrit (1802–1839) of Nodier's tale* Trilby *(1822): the music was by Jean Schneitzhoeffer (1787–1852); the choreography by Filippo Taglioni (1777–1871); the scenery by Pierre Cicéri (1782–1868); and the costumes by Eugène Lami (1800–1890).*

*Lami's white muslin costume for* La Sylphide *with the pink tights, satin shoes and pale blue gauze wings, was the first of a long line of similar costumes conceived by other artists in this moonlight style for the* ballet blanc *of the Romantic period. In fact the* tutu, *or short dancing skirt with numerous layers of material, which became the conventional costume of the* danseuse *right down to the time of Diaghilev, and is still in use, was derived from this particular dress worn by Taglioni in* La Sylphide.

*The ballet was first performed at the* Opéra, Paris, *on 12th March, 1832, and it appeared in London on 26th July of the same year at the Theatre Royal, Covent Garden. Its success in both cities was chiefly due to the great elasticity and purity of Marie Taglioni's dancing.*

*An earlier impression of this print was published in 1845 by J. Mitchell, 33 Old Bond Street, London, as one of six plates entitled* Souvenir d'Adieu de Marie Taglioni.

JONES, T. (working 1820–1836) and George HUNT (working 1824–1836).

**111** A scene in the ballet *Le Rossignol*, first performed at the King's Theatre, London, on 5th March, 1836. Published by Bell, 28 Craven Street, London, 1st June, 1836.

*Aquatint;* $5\frac{5}{8} \times 8\frac{5}{8}$          Enthoven Collection

*The choreography of this ballet was by Deshayes (working 1800–1842) and the music by J. B. Nadaud.*

*The print, of which the composition and etched outline were by Jones and only the aquatint by Hunt, appears to have been a book illustration. The dancers at the centre of the stage represent Jules Perrot (1800–after 1860) and Carlotta Grisi, here depicted for the first time in an English print.*

DEVÉRIA, Jacques Jean Marie Achille (1800–1857).

**112** Fanny Elssler as Florinda in Spanish costume in the ballet *Le Diable Boiteux*. Published as No. 29 of a series, by Aumont, Rue J. J. Rousseau No. 10, and by Rittner et Goupil. Boulevard Montmartre No. 15, Paris, *c.* 1838.

*Lithograph, coloured by hand;* $15 \times 9\frac{3}{8}$          Enthoven Collection

Le Diable Boiteux, *by Burat de Gurgy and Jean Coralli (1779–1854) with music by Casimir Gide (1804–1868), was produced at the* Opéra, *Paris, on 1st June, 1836, with the Viennese dancer, Fanny Elssler, in the part of Florinda. In London it was produced as* The Devil on Two Sticks *at Covent Garden in 1837, and a* divertissement *from it was put on in that year at the King's Theatre. The full ballet was produced under the title of* Le Diable Boiteux *at Her Majesty's Theatre on 9th August, 1838, with Fanny Elssler as Florinda, in the violet and black* cachucha *costume already made famous by Pauline Duvernay at Covent Garden in 1837. It was on this occasion that English audiences noticed a dramatic quality in Elssler's dancing that was new to the ballet.*

ANONYMOUS (second quarter of 19th century).

**113** Fanny Elssler as Sarah in the ballet *The Gypsy*. Title-page to a pianoforte score arranged by Henri Herz from the orchestral accompaniment to a dance (*La Cracovienne*) in *La Gypsy*, London, *c.* 1839.

*Lithograph;* $12\frac{3}{4} \times 7\frac{7}{8}$          Enthoven Collection

La Gypsy *was first produced at the* Opéra, *Paris, on 28th January, 1839, and in London at Her Majesty's Theatre on 25th July of the same year. The choreography was by F. Taglioni after Mazilier, and the music by François Benoist (1794–1878) and Ambroise Thomas (1811–1896).*

*As the architectural background suggests, the setting for the ballet was Scottish, and* La Cracovienne, *the most favoured dance in the performance, was supposed to take place in the market square of Edinburgh.*

BOUVIER, J. (working second quarter of 19th century).

**114** Marie Taglioni and A. Guerra in *L'Ombre*, a ballet in two acts, as danced at Her Majesty's Theatre, 18th June, 1840. From the series *Celebrated Opera Dancers of Her Majesty's Theatre*, after drawings by various artists, published by Thomas McLean, London, *c.* 1846.

*Lithograph, coloured by hand; cut to* $14\frac{3}{4} \times 11\frac{1}{2}$          E.2890–1948

*Originally in three acts, this ballet was first produced with Marie Taglioni in the chief role of Angela at St. Petersburg on 28th November, 1839. On that occasion the scenery was by Federov and other artists, and the costumes by Mathieu.*

*In the London production of 1840 Angela was a dream-character in the first act and a spirit in the second act, and in this role Taglioni exploited her extraordinary virtuosity by flitting like a white moth over the stage and alighting at times on such things as a rose bush. This particular effect was probably achieved, according to Madame Karsavina in* The Dancing Times *of February, 1954, by the device of the 'slipper', a hollow shaped to hold a pointed foot at the back of the structure supporting the rose bush.*

*Filippo Taglioni was responsible for the story and choreography of* L'Ombre: *the music was by Maurer. For the London production the scenery was designed by William Grieve (1800–1844).*

*An earlier version of this print was published by McLean on 15th July, 1840.*

BOUVIER, J. (working second quarter of 19th century).

**115** Carlotta Grisi and Jules Perrot in the ballet *La Esmeralda* at Her Majesty's Theatre, 1844. From the series *Celebrated Opera Dancers of Her Majesty's Theatre*, after drawings by various artists, published by Thomas McLean, London, *c.* 1846.

*Lithograph, coloured by hand; cut to* $14\frac{3}{4} \times 11\frac{3}{16}$          E.2892–1948

La Esmeralda, *produced on 9th March, 1844, at Her Majesty's Theatre, was probably the masterpiece of Jules Perrot as a choreographer. The story is that of Victor Hugo's romance* Notre-Dame de Paris *published in 1831, but the conception of the ballet as a whole owed much to the manager of Her Majesty's Theatre, Benjamin Lumley. The music by Cesare Pugni was written by the composer in London where he kept closely in touch with Lumley and Perrot. The scenery was designed by William Grieve, and the costumes by Madame Copère, who functioned both as a dancer at Her Majesty's Theatre from 1826 to 1847 and as wardrobe mistress during the later part of that period. Perrot's clothes in his role of Gringoire, the poet, are vaguely fifteenth century in style, as the story requires: the bodice and pigtails of Grisi, although quite anachronistic, are meant to indicate the gypsy character of Esmeralda. The two dancers are shown here in the* Truandaise, *a* pas de deux *in the first scene of the ballet.*

*An earlier version of this print was published by Thomas McLean on 6th April, 1844.*

BOUVIER, J. (working second quarter of 19th century).

**116** Carlotta Grisi and Jules Perrot in *La Polka* at Her Majesty's Theatre, 1844. From the series *Celebrated Opera Dancers of Her Majesty's Theatre*, after drawings by various artists, published by Thomas McLean, London, *c.* 1846.

*Lithograph, coloured by hand; cut to* $13\frac{7}{8} \times 10\frac{7}{8}$          E.2893–1948

*The polka originated in a Bohemian folk-dance first adopted as a social dance in Prague during 1835, to become the vogue in Paris during 1840. On 11th April, 1844, Perrot and Grisi, in stage versions of Bohemian national costumes, demonstrated the polka as a* divertissement *at Her Majesty's Theatre and are shown here executing Bohemian heel-steps. From that year until the end of the nineteenth century the polka in a modified form became one of the most popular ballroom dances in England.*

*This print was first published in May, 1844, by Thomas McLean. The tunic and bodice are coloured red in this example, but in others they are to be found sometimes coloured blue.*

ANONYMOUS (1845).

**117** Representation of a scene in the ballet *Éoline, ou la Fille de la Dryade*, as produced at Her Majesty's Theatre on 8th March, 1845. From *The Illustrated London News*, 15th March, 1845, Vol. 6, p. 168.

*Wood engraving;* $5\frac{3}{8} \times 6\frac{1}{8}$ Enthoven Collection

*The scenery for this sinister ballet was designed by Charles Marshall (1806–1890), and the scene represented here, with the haunted castle, suggests, quite appropriately, danger and loneliness, as well as dreaminess. A diagonal composition in which one side is nearly all mass and the other mainly void, would have been unusual before about 1840.*

*The ballet was in six scenes, the story and choreography being by Jules Perrot (1800– after 1860) and the music by Cesare Pugni (1798–1869). The part of Rübezahl, the gnome, was taken by Perrot himself, and that of Éoline, the Dryad, by Lucile Grahn.*

CHALON, Alfred Edward, R.A. (1780–1860).

**118** Carlotta Grisi, Marie Taglioni, Lucile Grahn and Fanny Cerrito in the *Pas de Quatre* composed by Jules Perrot, as danced at Her Majesty's Theatre on 12th July, 1845. From the series *Celebrated Opera Dancers of Her Majesty's Theatre*, after drawings by various artists, published by Thomas McLean, London, *c.* 1846.

*Lithograph, coloured by hand; cut to* $16\frac{3}{8} \times 13\frac{3}{4}$ E.2883–1948

*This* pas de quatre, *danced to the music of Cesare Pugni, was a great event in the history of the ballet, since it was conceived for, and executed by, four of the leading ballerinas of the Romantic period. It required all the tact of the manager of Her Majesty's Theatre, Benjamin Lumley, and all the skill of Perrot, the choreographer, to produce a* divertissement *in which the special gifts of each dancer were displayed without any of them seeming to have the chief part. The result was a technical and artistic triumph, applauded rapturously by the spectators and much praised by the critics. It was repeated three times in 1845, and revived in 1847 for two performances with Carolina Rosati replacing Lucile Grahn.*

*The costumes are in the style initiated by Eugène Lami for* La Sylphide: *pink tights, white muslin skirts and light pink bodices.*

*An earlier impression of this print was published in 1845 by J. Mitchell, 33 Old Bond Street, London, as one of six plates entitled* Souvenir d'Adieu de Marie Taglioni.

BRANDARD, John (1812–1863).

**119** Lucile Grahn as Catarina in the ballet *Catarina, ou La Fille du Bandit*, as first produced at Her Majesty's Theatre, London, on 3rd March, 1846. Published 21st April, 1846, by Messrs. Fores, 41 Piccadilly.

*Lithograph, coloured by hand;* $17\frac{5}{8} \times 10\frac{11}{16}$ Enthoven Collection

*The music of this ballet was by Cesare Pugni, the scenery by Charles Marshall and the choreography by Jules Perrot. The ballet was outstanding in its day for its atmosphere and for busy miming with swords and muskets.*

*An engraving related to this print, without the background, was made by A. H. Payne and published about the same time at Leipzig and Dresden with the title in German.*

SMYTH, ——, after Samuel READ (1816–1883).

120 Representation of the last scene (No. 5) in the ballet *Electra, ou la Pleiade Perdue*, as produced at Her Majesty's Theatre, London, on 17th April, 1849. From *The Illustrated London News*, 5th May, 1849, Vol. 14, p. 293.

*Wood engraving;* $7 \times 9\frac{1}{8}$                                      Enthoven Collection

*The scenery for* Electra, or the Lost Pleiad *was by Charles Marshall; and the last scene illustrated here has a peculiar significance in that electric light was employed in it, probably for the first time in the history of the stage. Carlotta Grisi took the role of Electra in her electric halo, being drawn up to join a group of suspended incarnations of the firmament, in a style recalling that of Blake or of some Romantic painter like Otto Runge.*

*The story and choreography of the ballet were by Paul Taglioni (1808–1884), brother of Marie Taglioni, and the music was by Cesare Pugni.*


VEIT, Louis (working mid-19th century), after Julien Raymond de BAUX (working *c.* 1856–1860).

121 Élise Casati as a Russian peasant girl in Paul Taglioni's comedy-ballet *The Adventures of Flick and Flock* at the Royal Opera House, Berlin. Plate 3 in *Album der Bühnen-Costüme* by Eduard Bloch, Vol. I, Berlin, 1859.

*Lithograph, coloured by hand;* $10\frac{9}{16} \times 5\frac{11}{16}$                          Library

The Adventures of Flick and Flock *was a comic fairy ballet in three acts, wherein two young men had adventures in various cities, including London, Berlin and St. Petersburg. Élise Casati is shown wearing a somewhat idealised contemporary Russian peasant costume, but this includes recognisable versions of the national headdress* (kokovschnik) *in red velvet decorated with pearls; the chemise decorated with gold braid; and the two skirts, which however are considerably shorter for dancing than those actually worn by Russian women. Silver spurs are to be seen on her shoes.*


VEIT, Louis (working mid-19th century).

122 Minna Kitzing and Anna Selling as English sailors in Paul Taglioni's comedy-ballet *The Adventures of Flick and Flock*, at the Royal Opera House, Berlin. Plate 6 in *Album der Bühnen-Costüme* by Eduard Bloch, Vol. I, Berlin, 1859.

*Lithograph, coloured by hand;* $10\frac{5}{16} \times 5\frac{11}{16}$                          Library

*This lithograph was drawn in the Veit studio after a photograph by L. Haase & Co., of Berlin.*

*Here is evidence of that fashion for costume* en travestie, *the beginnings of which can be traced back to the late eighteenth century (see Plate 71), and which runs parallel with the decline of the status of the male dancer during the nineteenth century, to survive in the principal boy of the modern English pantomime.*


VEIT, Louis (working mid-19th century).

123 Wilhelm Ebel as Count Morgano in Paul Taglioni's ballet *Morgano* at the Royal Opera House, Berlin. Plate 12 in *Album der Bühnen-Costüme* by Eduard Bloch, Vol. I, Berlin, 1859.

*Lithograph, coloured by hand;* $10\frac{5}{16} \times 5\frac{3}{4}$                          Library

*This lithograph was drawn in the Veit studio after a photograph by R. Marovsky.*

*By the middle of the nineteenth century the Germans were taking considerable trouble to render historical costumes accurately. Ebel is shown wearing a dark red tunic and hose, a coat of mail, a dark brown cloak and a helmet with a red plume. The plaited hair and the moustache complete the semi-oriental appearance of the dancer as a mediaeval Hungarian nobleman.*

VEIT, Louis (working mid-19th century).

**124** Nadejda Bogdanova in the title-role of Jules Perrot's ballet *La Esmeralda* in St. Petersburg, *c.* 1856–1859. Plate 18 in *Album der Bühnen-Costüme* by Eduard Bloch, Vol. I, Berlin, 1859.

*Lithograph, coloured by hand;* $10\frac{5}{16} \times 5\frac{13}{16}$          Library

*This lithograph was drawn in the Veit studio after a photograph by R. Marovsky.*

*The career of Bogdanova, who had been trained in Paris and had previously danced with great success there and in Vienna, is significant in the history of the ballet in Russia, because it represents the emergence of the Russian-born* prima ballerina *at a time when this position was usually held by foreigners. Bogdanova appeared in St. Petersburg in 1856: Perrot came to the city in 1848, and left it in 1859. Russian dancers had already acquired a reputation for their classical technique, but not for any particularly Russian style of dancing. No such style had yet emerged from the status of folk art.*

WILHELM, Charles (pseudonym of William John Charles PITCHER, R.I.) (1858–1925).

**125** Design for the costume of Miss Richards, a dancer in *The Coral Island Ballet* in Act III of *The Black Crook*, as produced at the Alhambra Theatre, London, in December, 1881. One of a series.

*Pen, ink and water-colour;* $5\frac{5}{8} \times 3\frac{3}{4}$          E.812–1932
Bequeathed by Mr. James S. Henderson.

*Coral motifs appear in the designs of the circlet and skirt. The costume is in three shades of rose-coloured pink.*

*The Black Crook was a Fairy Opera, first produced in 1872. The story was based by Harry Paulton on that of the* Biche au Bois: *the music was by Frederick Clay (1838–1889) and Georges Jacobi (1840–1906).*

*This and the following designs (Plates 126–128) are drawn on tracing-paper pasted into books, with many others of the same sort. They were no doubt Wilhelm's duplicates made for use in the wardrobe workshops.*

WILHELM, Charles (pseudonym of William John Charles PITCHER, R.I.) (1858–1925).

**126** Design for a dancer in the ballet *Fan-ta-sie* in the pantomime *Aladdin*, produced at Drury Lane Theatre, London, on 26th December, 1885. One of a series.

*Pen, ink, water-colour and gold paint;* $6\frac{13}{16} \times 2\frac{7}{8}$          E.1339–1932
Bequeathed by Mr. James S. Henderson.

*The design is in black, gold, turquoise and cobalt blue, and is not modelled on actual Chinese female costume. In fact the decorations simulating gold embroidery are Japanese*

*in character, and their appearance in this design can be attributed to the craze for Japanese decoration started in England by Whistler and the architect E. W. Godwin during the 1870s. Capricious and fantastic costumes were customary in pantomime, and some of the designs for* Aladdin *have even less associations with China than this one.*

*Aladdin was composed by E. L. Blanchard with music by Oscar Barrett. The ballets were invented by Madame Katti Lanner: the scenery was designed by Henry Emden and others, and the costumes by Wilhelm. The production was by Augustus Harris.*

WILHELM, Charles (pseudonym of William John Charles PITCHER, R.I.) (1858–1925).

**127** Design for the costume of a female dancer in the role of a swan. One of five designs made for a pantomime produced at the Alexandra Theatre, Liverpool, Christmas, 1885.

*Pen, ink and water-colour;* $5\frac{7}{8} \times 2\frac{7}{8}$            E.1276–1932
Bequeathed by Mr. James S. Henderson.

*At the end of the nineteenth and beginning of the twentieth centuries Wilhelm designed most of the costumes for pantomimes and* ballet-divertissements *at the Alhambra Theatre, London. He did similar work for pantomime companies on tour in the large provincial theatres, such as The Lyceum, Edinburgh, The Tyne Theatre, Newcastle, The Grand Theatre, Leeds, and the Theatre Royal, Manchester.*

*This drawing has Wilhelm's inscription beneath it stating that it was for a 'Swan Ballet', and it shows his clear, capable draughtsmanship at its best. It may be compared with Stern's design for bird costumes in the same tradition, reproduced in Plate 170.*

WILHELM, Charles (pseudonym of William John Charles PITCHER, R.I.) (1858–1925).

**128** Design for the costumes of three dancers in the roles of Shamrock, Rose and Thistle in the ballet *Rose d'Amour*, produced at the Empire Theatre, London, May, 1888.

*Pen, ink, water-colour and silver paint;* $6\frac{11}{16} \times 5\frac{11}{16}$       E.1497–1932
Bequeathed by Mr. James S. Henderson.

*The Shamrock costume is coloured in light and dark greens; that of the Rose in pink with dark green foliage; and that of the Thistle in violet with grey-green foliage.*

*These three dancers formed a group of national flowers in a* ballet-divertissement *which was performed as an interlude in a music hall programme, featuring Dan Leno and Marie Loftus. The ballet consisted of three tableaux, of which the first was entitled* Kingdom of the Flowers. *It was the invention of Madame Katti Lanner, with music by Hervé (pseudonym for Florimond Rougé, 1825–1892), and was produced under the direction of Augustus Harris. The scenery was by Henry Emden and T. E. Ryan, and the costumes by Wilhelm.*

BESCHE, Lucien (working 1883–1890).

**129** Design for the costume of a female dancer in a *ballet-divertissement* at the Alhambra Theatre, London. Signed, and dated 1890.

*Pen, ink and water-colour;* $8 \times 6\frac{5}{8}$           E.42–1948
Bequeathed by Mr. Henry Herbert Harrod.

*The costume is modelled on a Balkan (probably Greek) peasant costume of the nineteenth century.*

*At this date the scenery for the Alhambra ballets was painted by T. E. Ryan, and the music for them was generally composed or arranged by Georges Jacobi (1840–1906), conductor of the Theatre orchestra from 1872 to 1898. Lucien Besche also designed the borders of many of the Alhambra programmes.*

COMELLI, Attilio (*c.* 1858–1925).

**130** Design for the costume of a dancer in a *ballet-divertissement, c.* 1893. From a series of twenty-four costumes. Annotated in pencil on back and front of cardboard mount.

*Water-colour on tracing-paper;* 13¼×8          E.3326–1934
Given by Mrs. Arthur Collins.

*The costume is coloured blue with red and white decorations, and was one of a group for a ballet called* The Sleeper Awakened.

*Comelli, like Wilhelm, was regularly employed as a costume designer for entertainments at the Alhambra, Drury Lane and other London theatres at the end of the nineteenth and beginning of the twentieth centuries. Since there seems to be no record of* The Sleeper Awakened *being produced in London in 1893, it is quite probable that this is a design for a ballet in a pantomime produced at one of the big provincial theatres in that year.*

BENOIS, Alexander Nikolaievich (1870–1960).

**131** Design for the costume to be worn by Nijinsky as the slave of Armide in the ballet *Le Pavillon d'Armide*, produced at the Maryinsky Theatre, St. Petersburg, on 25th November, 1907. Signed and inscribed with notes by the artist.

*Pen, ink and water-colour;* 12½×5¾          E.632–1936

*The designs for* Le Pavillon d'Armide *were inspired by French court ballets of the eighteenth century. Both the conception of the costume and the style of the drawing itself combine an exotic impressionism with a kind of Rococo romanticism, in harmony with a mood, or moods, cultivated at this period.*

*The ballet, which was the first Russian ballet to be seen in France, was first performed by Diaghilev's company at the* Théâtre du Châtelet, *Paris, in 1909, with Anna Pavlova (1882–1931) and Vaslav Nijinsky (1890–1950). The scenario was by Benois, the music by Nicholas Tcherepnine (1873–1945), and the choreography by Michel Fokine (1880–1942).*

*Another version of the design for the Slave's costume, then in the possession of Mrs. Sophie Barou, was exhibited as No. 22 alongside the Museum drawing in the Diaghilev Exhibition at Edinburgh and London in 1954. A further version, used for the Paris production of the ballet, and then in the collection of Mr. H. Ison Porter, was shown as No. 23 alongside the others in the same exhibition (see Richard Buckle,* Catalogue of the Diaghilev Exhibition, *London, 1954, p. 14).*

ROERICH, Nicolai Konstantinovich (born 1874).

**132** A POLOVTSIAN CAMP AT DAWN. Design for the scene in *Polovtsian Dances from Prince Igor*, a ballet in one act, first produced by Diaghilev at the *Théâtre du Châtelet*, Paris, on 19th May, 1909. Signed by the artist.

*Tempera and body-colour;* 20×30          E.2487–1920
Presented by the Comité d'Honneur of the Roerich Exhibition, Goupil Gallery, 1920.

*Roerich also designed the costumes for this ballet, which proved to be one of the most popular of all those produced by Diaghilev. The choreography was by Michel Fokine, with music taken from the second act of Borodin's opera* Prince Igor.

*The design has a relaxed, careless quality, representing one of the many developments in pseudo-primitive stylisation that took place in the early twentieth century, and which found an appropriate medium in the Russian ballet.*

GONTCHAROVA, Natalia Sergeevna (1881–1962).

**133** Project for a backdrop in the opera-ballet *Le Coq d'Or*, produced by Diaghilev at the *Opéra*, Paris, on 24th May, 1914. Signed by the artist within and below the design.

*Water-colour;* 21×29                                                    E.287–1961

*Several versions of this design for a backdrop in* Le Coq d'Or *were made by Gontcharova, one of which shows a row of musicians in the foreground and behind them King Dodon, the Queen of Shemâkhan and others seated round a table, with a background like that in the present drawing (see* Catalogue of Diaghilev Exhibition, *1954, No. 141).*

*All the designs by Gontcharova for this ballet are homogeneous in style, and the project shows how drastically she broke from the sumptuous romanticism of Bakst (which might be called* post-fin-de-siècle *in feeling). Here the chief colours are shades of red, which Gontcharova was very fond of, using them with discordant emphasis alongside yellow and orange. Russian folk art, ikons, Cubism and Rayonnism have all contributed to the defiance of naturalism, and to a design which has an abrupt force on one plane only. The theme of the ballet itself was similarly forceful and may have seemed to the audiences of 1914 like some sparkling nightmare from an unknown corner of the past.*

*The music of* Le Coq d'Or *was by Rimsky-Korsakov and the choreography by Fokine. Its production opened the second phase of the Diaghilev Ballet, in which Gontcharova and Larionov, and later Massine, figured more prominently than Bakst, Fokine and Nijinsky.*

GONTCHAROVA, Natalia Sergeevna (1881–1962).

**134**
**135**
**136**
**137**
Designs (4) for costumes in the opera-ballet *Le Coq d'Or*, produced by Diaghilev at the *Opéra*, Paris, on 24th May, 1914. Signed, and annotated by the artist.

*Pencil, water- and body-colour; size of sheets* 15×10½      E.289, 294, 296, 297–1961

*These four costume designs, for a young peasant (E.294–1961), a young peasant woman (E.289–1961), an elderly peasant (E.297–1961) and elderly peasant woman (E.296–1961), are representative of the series of ten designs for costumes of minor characters in* Le Coq d'Or *which the Museum acquired from the artist in 1961 (E.288–297–1961). They appear to be more or less as used in the production, though other versions were made. Diaghilev was always highly critical, and Gontcharova very conscientious, with the result that designs for his productions, for example the project for the backdrop (Plate 133), were often re-drawn to incorporate slight alterations. The forms of the costumes and their decorations are based on Russian folk-costumes of fairly recent centuries, though transformed and made uniquely of their time and place by the jagged influence of Cubism and the hot colour schemes favoured by Gontcharova.*

RUTHERSTON, Albert Daniel (1881–1953).

**138** Design for the costume of Aurora in *The Awakening of Flora*, a ballet in one act performed by Madame Pavlova's company in New York, in 1914. Signed and inscribed by the artist.

*Pen, water-colour and gold paint;* $12\frac{1}{2} \times 5\frac{7}{8}$                                        E.208–1926

Le Reveil de Flore *was an anacreontic ballet with music by Riccardo Drigo (1846–1930) and choreography by Marius Petipa (1822–1910), first performed at the Maryinsky Theatre, St. Petersburg, in 1895. In the 1914 version, for which Rutherston designed both scenery and costumes, the choreography was by Ivan Clustine (1860–1941), Pavlova's* maître de ballet *during her American tour. Pavlova herself took the part of Flora.*

*The stylised outlines of the drawing are in the English taste and owe something to Beardsley as well as to the study of dancers on Greek pots; and possibly also to Isidora Duncan's eurhythmic dancing of the previous decade.*

STERN, Ernst Julian (1876–1954).

**139** THE MAGICIAN WU AND SIX CAPTIVES. Design for a scene in *Die Grüne Flöte*, a ballet produced by Max Reinhardt at the *Deutsches Theater*, Berlin, April, 1916. Signed by the artist.

*Lithograph;* $11\frac{7}{16} \times 17\frac{9}{16}$                                        E.1238–1937
Given by the artist.

Die Grüne Flöte *was written by Hugo von Hofmansthal for an arrangement by Nilson of music by Mozart. Stern, the designer of the settings, designed the scenery and costumes for numerous Reinhardt productions from 1906 to 1921, including* The Miracle.

*The rough, sensational style of the design owes something to the Expressionist movement, the influence of which was felt in central Europe at this date in all the arts.*

LARIONOV, Mikhail Fyodorovich (1881–1964).

**140** Design for the costume of a peasant woman in the ballet *Le Soleil de Nuit*, as produced by Diaghilev at the *Grand Théâtre*, Geneva, on 20th December, 1915. Signed and inscribed by the artist.

*Pencil, indian ink, water-colour and tinfoil with amendments pasted down.*
$16 \times 10\frac{1}{4}$                                        E.111–1961

*Soon after the outbreak of the 1914 War Diaghilev settled in Lausanne surrounded by various collaborators, including Larionov, Stravinsky and Massine, the last of whom was encouraged to try his hand at choreography under the tutelage of Larionov. The result of this experiment was* Le Soleil de Nuit, *a ballet with themes from Russian folk-lore and music from Rimsky-Korsakov's opera* Snegouroutchka (The Snowmaiden). *The novelty and variety of the dances in this immediately popular work put Massine on the map as a choreographer and promised much that was later fulfilled in him. It was also the first instance in which Larionov's original ideas about dancing were given a chance to influence practical choreography. His interest in dancing was almost lifelong, and a number of the books on this subject collected by him over the years were acquired in 1961 for the Museum Library.*

*Larionov's peasant-style costumes, against a backcloth of dark blue with ten orange-coloured sun-faces in the upper part, had a certain Fauve uncouthness overlaying a doll-like quality reminiscent of actual Russian dolls. The stiff arrested appearance of dolls is expressed also in the angular outlines of this design.*

GONTCHAROVA, Natalia Sergeevna (1881–1962).

**141** Design for the costume of a seahorse in the revival of the ballet *Sadko*, as produced by Diaghilev at the *Teatro Victoria Eugenia* in San Sebastian, Spain, in 1916. Signed by the artist.

*Pencil, water-colour, body-colour and tinfoil;* $7\frac{3}{4} \times 4$         E.320–1961

*The earlier ballet of* Sadko, *with music taken from Rimsky-Korsakov's opera of that name, has been described by Grigoriev* (The Diaghilev Ballet, *p. 53) as 'a rousing display of Russian temperament: . . . its final* ensemble *produced much the same effect as the dances from* Prince Igor'. *In the first version performed on 6th June, 1911, at the Théâtre du Châtelet, the choreography was by Fokine and the designs by Boris Anisfeldt. When in 1916 Diaghilev wished to revive the ballet it was found that Fokine's choreography was practically forgotten, so a new version was arranged with Anisfeldt's scenery, new costumes by Gontcharova and new choreography by Adolph Bolm, who had worked first with the Diaghilev Company in 1912. The second* Sadko *was first performed at San Sebastian and Bilbao in 1916 and later in the same year at the Metropolitan Opera, New York.*

*The locale of the ballet is the underwater world in which seahorses are to be found. Gontcharova's design has none of the submarine shades that might have been expected, but the warm colour and blunt forms typical of her own peculiar Neo-Primitivism with its reference to Russian folk art.*

LARIONOV, Mikhail Fyodorovich (1881–1964).

**142, 143** Designs (2) for costumes in the ballet *Kikimora*, as produced by Diaghilev at the *Teatro Victoria Eugenia*, San Sebastian, Spain, on 25th August, 1916. Both signed by the artist, and E.281–1961 dated *St. Sebastian 1916*.

*Pencil and body-colour*

**142** Kikimora.
$28\frac{3}{8} \times 16\frac{1}{2}$         E.280–1961

**143** The Cat.
$20\frac{3}{4} \times 14\frac{3}{8}$         E.281–1961

Kikimora *was first produced at San Sebastian as recorded above. Later, in April, 1917, at Rome, it was added to a group of similar ballets also based on Russian folk-tales—*Baba Yaga, Bova *and* Khorovod—*the whole series being entitled* Les Contes Russes *(see Plates 145, 146). In Paris this suite was performed first at the* Théâtre du Châtelet *in May, 1917, and later in the same year it appeared at Madrid. The music of* Les Contes Russes *was by Liadov, the choreography by Massine and the costumes and scenery by Larionov. Massine's rise to fame in the Diaghilev Company during the 1914 War marks a break with the nineteenth-century traditions which still guided the taste of Fokine.* Kikimora *was his third choreographic invention for Diaghilev, and in devising it he was much influenced by Larionov, then almost as much interested in dancing as in painting.*

*The vehement heavy-handedness of these drawings with their direct appeal outside the reasonableness of perspective and the refinements of naturalism, is of the genre Fauve in a context of Russian folk-lore. Kikimora was an evil spirit and the Cat was her guardian. Although Larionov's designs show a pioneering intuition of changes of direction in the arts, he was by nature too gay, perhaps, to evoke evil convincingly. His design for Kikimora's facial make-up in alternate stripes is ingenious, and the Cat's rocking-horse nostrils look nearly as savage as some Polynesian or African carving; but choreographic interpretation apart, his conception of Kikimora is more comically nasty than sinister, and the Cat appears more impious than dangerous.*

LARIONOV, Mikhail Fyodorovich (1881–1964).

I44  Design for the costume of the Cricket in the ballet *Histoires Naturelles* first presented at Lausanne in 1916. Signed by the artist and inscribed by him in pencil *Pierre Bertin dans la rôle du Grillon. Costume mécanique aussi qui se met en mouvement exclusivement par la voix. Musique de Ravel Brevet No. 009721840536.*

*Pencil and water-colour;* $9 \times 14\frac{1}{4}$                                E.286–1961

*An imaginary patent number emphasises the humorous spirit in which this mechanical ballet was thought out. And yet it was also a serious attempt by the composer, Maurice Ravel (1875–1937), and Larionov, both of whom were interested in every kind of enterprise connected with the dance, to make choreography out of characteristic rhythms and movements of machines. The Cricket appears as if put together from a Meccano set, with legs and head constructed of triangular and rectangular surfaces, in the Cubist manner. For the settings, projections from coloured slides were intended. Presumably the stimulus behind this* jeu d'esprit *was the enthusiasm for machines proclaimed by the Futurists from 1909–1910 onwards. Histoires Naturelles was apparently never performed again after its trial for Diaghilev in 1916.*

*The design is coloured in shades of brown, bright yellow and orange, and is reproduced, along with one for a peacock in the same ballet, in Valentin Parnack's* Gontcharova: Larionov, *Paris, 1919.*

LARIONOV, Mikhail Fyodorovich (1881–1964).

I45  Design for a drop-curtain in the ballet *Les Contes Russes*, first performed at the *Teatro Costanzi*, Rome, in 1917. Signed and inscribed by the artist.

*Black chalk, water-colour and body-colour;* $16 \times 21$                        E.942–1927

Les Contes Russes *was the name given to the suite of small ballets, including* Kikimora *(see Plates 142, 143), first produced at San Sebastian in 1916. In the autumn and winter of that year at Rome, Liadov the composer, Massine the choreographer, and Larionov the designer, worked together upon the series which was first performed as* Les Contes Russes *at the* Teatro Costanzi *in April, 1917. In May, 1917,* Les Contes Russes *were performed in Paris at the* Théâtre du Châtelet, *and later, in 1917, at Madrid.*

*The drop-curtain design shows Bova Korolevich, a legendary Russian hero, encountering the dragon that guards the Swan Princess. It has the rugged outlines of a Fauve picture; but the whimsical side of that ruggedness, in the form of the white horse, for example, owes something to the study of Russian ikons, in which the horse of St. George is frequently stylised somewhat in this way. The stylised suggestion of movement in Byzantine and Russian painting was actually imitated in the choreography of the ballet, and the horse used by 'Korolevich' was a wooden one, partly because Diaghilev insisted that a living horse never looked real on the stage.*

LARIONOV, Mikhail Fyodorovich (1881–1964).

**146** THE MAGIC POOL. Design for the stage set of Scene II in the ballet *Les Contes Russes*, first produced by Diaghilev at the *Teatro Costanzi*, Rome, in 1917. Signed, and dated 1916.

*Body-colour; 22×30*                                                                                        E.1026–1926
Given by Dr. W. A. Propert.

*Scene I of* Les Contes Russes *embodied the original ballet of Kikimora, first produced in Spain in 1916 (see Plates 142, 143). Scene II introduced the story of the Swan Princess, and was part of the extended series of small ballets forming* Les Contes Russes *which Liadov, Massine and Larionov worked upon in Rome towards the end of 1916.*

*More than any other ballet-design by Larionov in the Museum collection this one shows certain mannerisms, such as the long intersecting planes of the pool, which have come to be associated with Rayonnism. This art movement was based on theories propounded by Larionov in Moscow in 1911, and subsequently. It had affinities with Cubism, but took its name from Larionov's preoccupation with the rays that emanate from objects, and the intangible forms resulting from the apparent conflict of these rays in space.*

LARIONOV, Mikhail Fyodorovich (1881–1964).

**147** Sketch of Gontcharova, Diaghilev, Massine and Beppo at a restaurant table. On the back is the menu of the restaurant *Au Petit Saint-Benoit* in Paris. Signed in pencil with initials of the artist and inscribed with the names of three sitters. *c.* 1917.

*Pencil, $8\frac{3}{4}\times10\frac{7}{8}$*                                                                            E.277–1961

*Léonide Massine joined the Diaghilev Company in 1913 at the age of seventeen, just after Diaghilev's quarrel with Nijinsky, and he made his début as a dancer in* La Legende de Joseph *in the following year. He left Diaghilev in 1920 and returned to the Company in 1924, but the last time he seems to have been actively associated with Larionov was in May, 1917, when* Les Contes Russes *were produced in Paris (see note on Plate 145). Beppo, the Italian who was for many years Diaghilev's valet, entered his service around 1910 and left it in the very early 1920s. Natalia Gontcharova met Larionov at the School of Painting, Sculpture and Architecture in Moscow about 1900; she met Diaghilev in 1913 and settled in Paris in 1915, and there she shared a studio with Larionov in the Rue Visconti. At the time when this drawing was made—as she herself pointed out when it was acquired for the Museum—she had become rather fat; but in after years she grew thin and frail. Serge Diaghilev was born in Perm in the province of Novgorod on 19th March, 1872, and died on 19th August, 1929, in Venice. From these various facts it seems reasonable to date the drawing about May, 1917, when all the people represented would have been found together in Paris.*

NASH, Paul (1889–1946).

**148** Design for the stage setting (The Great Hall of Vere Castle) in *The Truth about the Russian Dancers*, a balletic play produced at the Coliseum, London, on 15th March, 1920. Signed and inscribed by the artist.

*Pencil and water-colour; $23\frac{1}{2}\times15\frac{1}{2}$*                                                           E.933–1922
Presented by 'Some Friends of the Museum'.

*The play, or playlet, was written in a whimsical, ironic vein in 1919 by Sir James Barrie (1860–1937) for Tamara Karsavina, who invented the choreography of the dancing episodes in it for music composed by Sir Arnold Bax (1883–1953). The scene represents the hall in one of the stately homes of England, where the atmosphere has been changed owing to the disturbing presence of a guest from the Russian Ballet (Karissima: see Plate 149). Paul Nash's set, which disconcerted the conservative Barrie, has none the less a very English appearance, both in the character of the hall and in the sharp, brittle qualities of the drawn forms.*

*The play was revived in 1926.*

NASH, Paul (1889–1946).

**149** Design for the costume of Tamara Karsavina as Karissima in the balletic play, *The Truth about the Russian Dancers*, produced at the Coliseum, London, on 15th March, 1920. Signed, dated 1920 and inscribed by the artist.

*Pencil and water-colour;* $9\frac{1}{2} \times 6$           E.616–1928
Given by Mr. Rupert Mason.

The Truth about the Russian Dancers *was unusual in being primarily a playlet with threads of choreography running through it (see Plate 148). The balletic part was acted mainly by Karsavina as Karissima, whose medium of expression was choreographic only. Everyone else in the cast (with the exception of the* corps de ballet *who came on at the end) spoke in the normal way, but when Karissima was spoken to she danced a reply. Nash's design for her costume was reproduced in colour as Plate LXXXV in* Robes of Thespis, *edited for Rupert Mason by George Sheringham and R. Boyd Morrison, London, 1928.*

NASH, Paul (1889–1946).

**150** Design for the costume worn by members of the *corps de ballet* in *The Truth About the Russian Dancers*, produced at the Coliseum, London, on 15th March, 1920. Signed, dated 1920 and inscribed by the artist.

*Pencil and water-colour;* $10\frac{5}{8} \times 7\frac{1}{8}$           E.617–1928
Given by Mr. Rupert Mason.

*The drawings of the figures and their shadows in this design and in E.616–1928 (Plate 149) have been cut out and pasted down on paper, and in E.617 a pencilled background has been added on the supporting paper. This drawing was reproduced in half-tone as Plate LXXXVI in* Robes of Thespis, *edited for Rupert Mason by George Sheringham and R. Boyd Morrison, London, 1928.*

*While the hooped skirts are meant to recall the skirts of the Romantic period, their embellishments have a delicate meagreness that was the hall-mark of Paul Nash, more especially in the field of book production.*

LARIONOV, Mikhail Fyodorovich (1881–1964).

**151, 152** Designs (2) for costumes in the ballet *Chout* (*Le Buffon*) first produced by Diaghilev at the *Théâtre Gaîté-Lyrique*, Paris, on 17th May, 1921. E.282–1961 signed in pen by the artist: E.283–1961 signed in pen and dated [1]915 and inscribed by him in pencil. Both variously inscribed and stamped on the backs.

*Pencil and water-colour on two joined sheets*

**151** The Merchant (Le Marchand)
$27\frac{1}{4} \times 14\frac{3}{4}$           E.282–1961

**152** The Chief Clown (Le Buffon)
$26\frac{3}{4} \times 18\frac{3}{4}$           E.283–1961

Chout *was the French phonetic equivalent of the Russian* Shût, *meaning 'Buffoon'. The ballet was a small one in six scenes, with music by Serge Prokofiev, and scenery and costumes by Larionov, who also invented the scenario. As the date inscribed on the design for the Clown reveals, work on this ballet must have begun at Lausanne in 1915. Some of the other designs by Larionov for* Chout, *which were exhibited at New York in 1922, were also inscribed 'Lausanne, 1915' (see C. Brunion,* The Gontcharova-Larionov Exhibition, *New York, 1922).*

*The integration of the ballet does not appear to have been begun until after Massine broke with Diaghilev early in 1921, when the choreography was undertaken by the dancer Thadée Slavinsky under Larionov's supervision while the Diaghilev company was in Madrid. Work was finished on it at Monte Carlo just before it appeared for the first time in Paris in May.* Chout *was not well received: indeed Grigoriev and Lifar have both recorded their disapproval of the choreography, and Diaghilev was disappointed with it. This was a pity, because Larionov's costume designs (of which the semi-Rayonnist, semi-Cubist Chief Clown, as danced by Slavinsky, was the most grotesque) were unique in style for their date and function. More finished, but less vivid, versions of them were also made by Larionov (see* Jar-Ptitza, *No. 12, pp. 28, 29; and Hiler Harzburg's* Slapstick and Dumbbell, *Paris, 1924). The cast consisted of other clowns, wives of clowns, daughters of clowns and some soldiers; and the theme included a strong element of bourgeois-baiting of the kind Larionov was then associated with.*

*A projected design for the curtain was reproduced in colour in a volume by Gontcharova and others entitled* Les Ballets Russes *(Belvès, 1955, p. 81).*

BAKST, Léon Nikolaievitch (pseudonym for Lev Samoilovitch Rosenberg) (1866–1924).

153–156   Designs (4) for costumes in the ballet *The Sleeping Princess*, first produced by Diaghilev on 2nd November, 1921, at the Alhambra Theatre, London. Signed and dated: E.1106–1922, *1920*, E.1105, 1107, 1108–1922, *1921*.

*Pencil and water-colour*

**153**   Innocent Ivan.
$19\frac{1}{4}\times 12\frac{7}{8}$                                                                E.1105–1922

**154**   King Florestan XXIV.
$11\frac{9}{16}\times 6\frac{1}{2}$                                                                E.1106–1922

**155**   The Fairy of the Mountain Ash.
$11\frac{3}{8}\times 8\frac{3}{4}$                                                                E.1107–1922

**156**   Columbine.
$11\frac{3}{8}\times 8\frac{3}{4}$                                                                E.1108–1922

The Sleeping Princess *was the name given to Diaghilev's revival in 1921 of* La Belle au Bois Dormant, *first produced at the Maryinsky Theatre, St. Petersburg, on 3rd January, 1890. The story was based on Perrault's fairy tale of the same subject, which had been used previously in the nineteenth century for ballets of this name. In the 1890 production the music was by Tchaikovsky, the scenery and costumes by Vsevolojsky, Director of the Russian Imperial Theatres, and the choreography by Marius Petipa (1822–1910). When Diaghilev revived this famous ballet Petipa's choreography was employed again, with additions by Nijinska, and Tchaikovsky's score was in part re-orchestrated by Stravinsky. Bakst's contribution transformed the visual character of the ballet and the production was in fact the most lavish undertaken by Diaghilev. But the result was not a financial success. Sir Oswald Stoll, then manager of the Alhambra Theatre, seized the costumes and sets as securities, and Diaghilev had to pay off his debt to Stoll from the proceeds of his seasons at the Coliseum in 1924 and 1925.*

*The style of Bakst was very personal, with an* Art Nouveau *strain and a sophisticated garishness inspired by Near Eastern art. His use of bright, succulent colours together set up a vogue for such combinations as cerise and apple-green in the decorative schemes of clothes and furniture around 1910 and for some years afterwards. The dress designs of Paul Poiret bear witness to the impression made upon fashionable Parisians by the Russian Ballet and by the visual effects of Bakst in particular.*

*Bakst was of Jewish origin, and one of the most sensuous draughtsmen of the human figure ever known: his costume designs are always excellent because he imagined so intensely the body beneath each one and felt precisely how to enhance it by clothes appropriate to the stage and especially to dancing. They are suave and neat and clear, and as guides to the wardrobe workshops they must have been the best of their period.*

*Bakst was first associated with Diaghilev in 1899 in work for the art magazine* Mir Isskoustva (*The World of Art*). *His first designs for the Diaghilev Company were those for* Cléopâtre, *produced in Paris in 1909. Other famous ballets in which he collaborated were* Shéhérazade (*1910*), La Spectre de la Rose (*1911*), L'Après Midi d'un Faune (*1912*), *and* Les Femmes de Bonne Humeur (*1917*). *His designs for the costumes in* The Sleeping Princess *were made after studying eighteenth-century designs for court ballets, and, beautiful though they are, they scarcely illustrate the work of Bakst at his most sumptuous; rather at his most restrained point. The unconvincing primitivism of the design for Innocent Ivan seems to owe something to Gontcharova; for Bakst, unlike his younger rival of the* avant-garde, *was not inspired directly by Russian popular art.*

*The scenery for* The Sleeping Princess *was intentionally reminiscent of the Baroque theatrical stage designs by the Galli da Bibiena family (working 1680–1780: see Plates 48, 56 and 63).*

*The design for* Columbine, *one of Bakst's finest drawings, is reproduced in colour in* A Dictionary of Modern Ballet, *London, 1959, p. 46.*

LARIONOV, Mikhail Fyodorovich (1881–1964).

**157** Design for the costume of the Fox as a pilgrim in the ballet *Renard*, as produced by Diaghilev at the *Opéra*, Paris, on 18th May, 1922. Signed by the artist, and inscribed with a note in pencil.

*Water-colour;* $15\frac{5}{8} \times 11\frac{3}{8}$                                        E.278–1961

*Renard was unusual in being an opera with the action danced on the stage in conjunction with a performance by singers in the orchestra pit. Based on a Russian folk-tale about a cock who outwits an astute and wicked fox, the ballet gave Larionov the opportunity to express an amusing, childlike side of his nature not openly declared in his Rayonnist works. The style of his drawings for both sets and costumes is subfusc in colour and almost Impressionist, and at the same time roughly descriptive. The score by Stravinsky was in the style of his first phase and strongly indebted to Russian folk music.*

*This opera-ballet was originally commissioned from Stravinsky by Winnaretta, Princess Edmond de Polignac, the daughter of Isaac Merritt Singer. Her second husband, Edmond de Polignac, had been a composer, and she became one of the leading patrons of* avant-garde *music and art in Paris during the first quarter of the twentieth century.* Les Noces (*see Plates 158, 159*) *was first performed at her house in 1923.*

*The choreography of the 1922 version of* Renard *was by Bronislava Nijinska. In a revised version produced by Diaghilev in 1929 acrobatic passages were introduced* requiring acrobats to double with the dancers in the various roles. This new choreography was by Lifar, influenced considerably by Larionov.

Another costume design for this ballet by the same artist, and not reproduced, shows the Fox as a woman (E.279–1961).


GONTCHAROVA, Natalia Sergeevna (1881–1962).

**158** Design for Scene IV (The Wedding Feast) in the ballet, *Les Noces*, produced by Diaghilev at the *Théâtre Gaîté-Lyrique*, Paris, on 13th July, 1923. Signed by the artist with initials and dated [1]923 on the drawing, and in full on the mount.

*Pen, indian ink and water-colour;* $10\frac{3}{4} \times 17\frac{1}{2}$            E.321–1961

*Stravinsky conceived the idea of this ballet late in 1914 and had outlined the music for it by 1917. The choreographer was Nijinska, who in conjunction with Gontcharova and Larionov, embodied Diaghilev's notion of a ballet of stylised movement based on the arrested movements suggested by ikons. Stravinsky had scored the ballet for four pianos, woodwind and percussion, and the four pianos (two of which are represented in the drawing) had to be accommodated on the stage. Gontcharova's scenery was 'highly effective', says Grigoriev 'as a background for the dancers' in this unconventional ballet. 'It consisted of a plain backcloth and wings, together with one or two central "flats", in which windows of varying colours were inserted to indicate changes of place.' (The Diaghilev Ballet, p. 186). In this instance Gontcharova abandoned the hot and headlong style, which had seemed so personal in the* Coq d'Or *designs, and worked out sets of marked austerity, wherein the indirect influence of Gordon Craig is perhaps more evident than in any other design reproduced in this book. The hesitant drawing in black and brown suggests that this kind of stage arrangement did not come naturally to her at first: the scenery was very successful nevertheless. Another drawing of the same design is reproduced in* A Dictionary of Modern Ballet, *London, 1959, p. 44.*

*Craig, who was the son of the architect Edward W. Godwin and the actress Ellen Terry, was the only English artist to have a far-reaching effect on the continental stage during the first half of the twentieth century. Productions by him had appeared in London, Berlin and Moscow in the years before the 1914 War, and at that time he had communicated by means of his journal* The Mask *some of his innovations in the principles of stagecraft. Opposed not only to naturalism, but to obstreperous and over-decorative sets which intruded on action, he evolved his own style of token scenery and suggestive lighting, in order to establish the dominant mood of a play.*


GONTCHAROVA, Natalia Sergeevna (1881–1962).

**159** A group of male dancers. Design for costumes and choreography in the ballet *Les Noces*, first produced by Diaghilev at the *Théâtre Gaîté-Lyrique*, Paris, on 13th July, 1923. Signed by the artist.

*Indian ink;* $17\frac{3}{8} \times 13\frac{3}{8}$            E.105–1961

*The theme of this ballet is a Russian peasant wedding. The music was by Stravinsky, the designs by Gontcharova (see also Plate 158) and the choreography by Bronislava Nijinska. But both Gontcharova and Larionov contributed their views on the choreography, and the drawing shows how the grouping of the performers was considered in relation to the costumes, all of which were in black and white. Most of the dancing was in groups.*

*In comparison with all that had gone before the ballet was most unusual, with its choreographic forms inspired by sport, by geometry and by the angular stylisations of Russian ikons; with its purist costumes and sets, its incorporation of choral passages sung in Russian, and above all its convulsive music, in which the influence of jazz was prominent. Its success with the Paris public in 1923 was immense but was not maintained at that pitch by performances in after years.*

*Other costume designs by Gontcharova for this ballet, which are not reproduced, are Nos. E.106-110-1961 in the Print Room.*

BRAQUE, Georges (1882–1963).

**160** Design for a scene in *Les Fâcheux*, a ballet in one act from the comedy-ballet of Molière, first produced by Diaghilev at Monte Carlo on 19th January, 1924.

*Pencil and water-colour;* $8\frac{1}{2} \times 13$             E.959–1927

*The ballet was by Kochno, the music by Georges Auric, the choreography by Bronislava Nijinska and the scenery and costumes by Braque.*

*The opaque style of painting originated by Braque and the Cubists adapted itself well to the requirements of stage décor, apart from giving an extra sensation of dash and 'distortion' which was still new to audiences at the time.*

*This design does not seem to have been used. It is, however, reproduced together with the design that was used for the set, in* Les Fâcheux *by Jean Cocteau etc., Paris, 1924.*

BRAQUE, Georges (1882–1963).

**161, 162** Designs (2) for costumes in *Les Fâcheux*, a ballet in one act from the comedy-ballet of Molière, first produced by Diaghilev at Monte Carlo on 19th January, 1924. From a series of fifteen designs (E.944–958–1927).

*Pencil and water-colour*

**161** Design (front and back) for the *premier masque* (female).
$12 \times 18\frac{13}{16}$             E.958–1927

**162** Design (front and back) for the *deuxième masque* (male).
$12 \times 18\frac{13}{16}$             E.954–1957

*The free style of these drawings is characteristic of Braque and very pleasant in itself, though barely adequate for its purpose. Bodice and skirt in the first design are raw sienna; stockings and sleeves light blue. In the man's costume the front sides of the sleeves and breeches are light blue, and the doublet black with deep blue chevrons; but the back view shows doublet, cloak and breeches all coloured light red. During the second quarter of the twentieth century the use by Braque and Picasso of limited and earthy palettes was widely reflected in most of the applied arts.*

*Both designs are reproduced in* Les Fâcheux *by Jean Cocteau etc., Paris, 1924.*

POLUNIN, Vladimir (1880–1957).

**163** ST. GEORGE AND THE DRAGON. Design for a drop-curtain for Diaghilev's season of Russian ballet at the Coliseum, London, 1925. Signed by the artist.

*Water-colour;* $10\frac{1}{8} \times 14\frac{3}{4}$             E.480–1926

*This design, which was almost wholly inspired by the works of Russian ikon painters of the sixteenth and seventeenth centuries, was reproduced in Huntly Carter's* The New Spirit in the European Theatre, *London, 1925. Another version of it was reproduced as*

164. NATALIA GONTCHAROVA. Design for a backcloth in *L'Oiseau de Feu*, 1926. Coloured drawing.

*the frontispiece to Polunin's* The Continental Method of Scene Painting, *London, 1927. In his book the artist explained the advantages of painting scenery horizontally on a studio floor, instead of vertically on frames, as was still done in England in the first quarter of the twentieth century. By the continental method the nuances of a designer's style could be more faithfully rendered, and a thinner priming could be used, which made storage and transit less troublesome.*

*Much of the scenery for Diaghilev's productions after 1918 in London, Monte Carlo and Paris was made by Vladimir Polunin, assisted by his wife Elizabeth Polunin. In 1928 Polunin became head of the Department of stage-painting at the Slade School of Art in London.*


GONTCHAROVA, Natalia Sergeevna (1881–1962).

**164** Design for the backcloth of Scene II in the ballet *L'Oiseau de Feu* as produced at the Lyceum Theatre, London, on 25th November, 1926. Signed in ink by the artist.

*Pen, water-colour and gold, with pasted down amendments;* 24×26¼   E.2137–1932
Given by Dr. W. A. Propert.

The Firebird (*L'Oiseau de Feu*) *was founded on a Russian fairy-tale and was first produced by Diaghilev at the Paris Opéra on 25th June, 1910, with one set only by Golovin and with costumes by Golovin and Bakst. This design was part of the work commissioned by Diaghilev from Gontcharova for the reprise of 1926. Its wallpaper flatness, which is given a unity of style by the primitive drawing, itself gives to the scene a dreamlike quality suggesting an enormous and boundless Russian city.*

*The choreography of the ballet was by Fokine and the music by Stravinsky. It was the composer's first full-length ballet commission, and although the score had echoes of the manner of Rimsky-Korsakov it broke sufficiently with tradition to be regarded as utterly and alarmingly novel in 1910. Indeed Pavlova refused to have anything to do with the ballet, and the Firebird was danced originally by Karsavina. In 1926 this part was danced by Lydia Lopokhova, with Serge Lifar as Ivan Tsarevitch.*


KOROVIN, Konstantin Alexeievitch (1861–1939).

**165** Design for the costume of Laurent Novikoff in a *ballet-divertissement* in the opera *La Gioconda* performed by Madame Pavlova's company at the Royal Opera House, Covent Garden, London, in 1927. Signed and inscribed in Russian by the artist.

*Pencil and water-colour with gold and silver paint;* 12⅝×8½   E.13–1932

La Gioconda *was first produced in 1876, with music by Ponchielli. The choreography of the divertissement as performed in 1927 was by Ivan Clustine. Korovin, who designed the costumes, introduced here the mineral style of the Cubists, in the manner most frequently adopted in textile decoration of the 1920s, whether for clothes or for carpets.*


EXTER, Alexandra (1882–1949).

**166** Design for a stage setting in the ballet *Don Juan*, as produced at the *Opernhaus*, Cologne, in 1927. Signed by the artist.

*Body-colour;* 17¾×23¾   E.1594–1953
Given by Mr. Simon Lissim in memory of the artist.

*The Constructivist movement, of which Vladimir Tatlin, Naum Gabo and Antoine Pevsner were the best-known exponents, flourished mainly in Russia just before and just after the Revolution of 1917, especially in the theatre. Madame Exter, who was born in Kiev, designed settings and costumes in this style for productions in Russia, Italy, France and Germany during the second and third decades of the twentieth century. Some of her work at its best is reproduced in Gregor's and Fülöp-Miller's* Das Russische Theater, Zürich, 1927, *Raymond Cogniat's* Décors de Théâtre, Paris, 1930, *and the* Enciclopedia dello Spettacolo.

*Exter had a strong sense of rectilinear planes in three-dimensional patterns. Her later sets were designed like buildings, or rather like scaffoldings, where actors and dancers could appear significantly at different levels, on steps, fly-overs and platforms which had a token or symbolic value in accordance with the teachings of Gordon Craig (see Plate 158). Like those of most Constructivists, Exter's designs verged towards abstraction by way of geometrical purism, but they were distinguished by her taste in the use of opaque colour contrasts. In this design the pavilion structures are painted lacquer red and maroon with black roofs, against a background of sea-green. The steps are pale yellow and green, the platform pale yellow and the ground a dark mushroom brown.*


EXTER, Alexandra (1882–1949).

**167**  Design for a costume in the ballet *Don Juan*, as produced at the *Opernhaus*, Cologne, in 1927. Signed by the artist.

*Pencil and body-colour;* $21\frac{3}{8} \times 11\frac{1}{4}$           E.1597–1953
Given by Mr. Simon Lissim in memory of the artist.

*This drawing is characteristic of costume designs by Exter (see also Gregor and Fülöp-Miller,* Das Russische Theater, Zürich, 1927, *Plates 198–200) in which the outlines are almost geometrical and the forms conceived in Constructivist terms of solid geometry. The result here is curious: the design has a period flavour, not of the sixteenth century so much as of the 1920s. For instance, the bobbed hair and the pointed shoes, unlike the scholarly reincarnations of Bakst and Benois, show little understanding of the period intended. Apart from the collar and the lines of decoration on the doublet which are white, and the face and hands which are flesh-coloured, the costume is black.*


BENOIS, Alexander Nikolaievich (1870–1960).

**168**  Preliminary sketch for a scene in the ballet *Les Noces de l'Amour et Psyché*, produced at the *Opéra*, Paris, in 1928, by Mademoiselle Ida Rubinstein. Inscribed by the artist *Iʳᵉ idée l'Apothéose*, and dated 6th November, 1927. Also inscribed by him on the back with details of the production.

*Water-colour;* $11\frac{1}{8} \times 17\frac{7}{8}$           E.633–1936

*Ida Rubinstein was a rich amateur of the ballet who was sufficiently trained to dance and mime leading parts in Diaghilev's* Cléopâtre (1909) *and* Shéhérazade (1910). *It was her ambition to have a company of her own in which she was the leading dancer. In 1928 she formed such a company, and from then onwards for several years produced ballets with the collaboration of Stravinsky, Ravel, Fokine, Massine and other notable composers and choreographers. Although a picturesque personality of great physical attractions, and a born mime, her dancing technique never developed to the point of mastery, which limited the scope of the ballets she produced for herself as the central figure.*

*The music of* Les Noces de l'Amour et Psyché *was by Bach arranged by Arthur Honegger (1892–1955), and the choreography by Bronislava Nijinska. In this design Benois has not moved far from the spirit of his 1907 designs for* Le Pavillon d'Armide *(see Plate 131).*

LÉGER, Fernand (1881–1955).

**169** Design for a stage set in a ballet projected by Léonide Massine in 1932. Signed and dated by the artist.

*Water-colour;* $7\frac{3}{4} \times 9\frac{3}{8}$                                                       E.800–1939

*Léger exhibited with the Cubists as early as 1911, but by 1920 had evolved his own style inspired largely by machinery. In the course of his development, in which this drawing comes about mid-way, his touch was gradually relaxed and he began to show interest in organic forms. Here the forms are not particularly mechanistic, and since we do not know what the subject of the ballet was, their significance is not clear. The use of heavy outlines holding in opaque and intense colours characterises nearly all his works, and in different degrees those of many painters of the* École de Paris *who were influenced by the ideas of the* Fauves *before the 1914 War.*

*Léger designed the sets for various ballets, among others* La Création du Monde *for the Swedish Ballet in 1923.*

STERN, Ernst Julian (1876–1954).

**170** Design for the costumes of the chorus of birds in Act I of *Enchanted Night*, a ballet on ice, first performed at the Royal Opera House, Covent Garden, London, on 26th October, 1937. Signed and inscribed by the artist.

*Body-colour on blue paper;* $14 \times 22$                                             E.1208–1937
Given by the artist.

*During the early 1920s Stern was an art director in Ernst Lubitsch's film company. Later he came to London, when he designed the scenery and costumes for a number of musical entertainments, such as* Bitter Sweet *(1929) and* White Horse Inn *(1931). His design for the bird costumes follows the English tradition of popular ballet that survived from the great days of pantomime into a period of revues and variety shows. The passage of time is indicated clearly in the elongated figures of the bird dancers and in the perfunctory way in which the details of the costumes are rendered.*

GONTCHAROVA, Natalia Sergeevna (1881–1962).

**171**
**172** Designs (2) for costumes in the ballet *La Foire de Sorotchinsky*, as produced by the *Ballet Russes de Paris* at the *Salle Pleyel*, Paris, in August, 1940. Signed in pen and annotated by the artist in pencil and pen.

*Pencil, pen and water-colour; size of boards* $18\frac{1}{2} \times 8$                       E.304, 317–1961

*The style of these designs, one for a young peasant (E.304–1961) and one for a young peasant woman (E.317–1961) is fairly typical of the series of costume drawings for* The Fair at Sorochinsk *acquired from the artist in 1961 (E.299-319-1961). It is more naturalistic than her former work for the ballet and suggests that with late middle-age a certain over-compromising positivism affected her approach. In any case, when they were done the heyday of pioneering had passed, and the atmosphere in which* Le Coq d'Or *and* Les Noces *had startled Paris had disappeared with Diaghilev.*

*The costumes are based on late nineteenth-century styles. Here and there in the designs for the women, and in some of those for the men where embroidery is indicated, there remains something of the colour clash of Gontcharova's prime.*

*Some other designs and different versions of costumes in this ballet are reproduced in colour in* A Dictionary of Modern Ballet, *London, 1959, p. 167.*

GONTCHAROVA, Natalia Sergeevna (1881–1962).

**173** Design for a stage setting for the ballet *La Foire de Sorotchinsky* (The Fair at Sorochinsk), as produced by the *Ballets Russes de Paris* at the *Salle Pleyel*, Paris, in August, 1940. Signed by the artist.

*Water- and body-colour;* $25\frac{3}{4} \times 32$                                    E.298–1961

*The theme of this ballet was taken from a story by Gogol entitled* Evening on a Farm near Dekanka. *For one version the choreography was by Georges Balanchine: for another version it was by Elstor; in both cases for music adapted from Moussorgsky's opera of the same name first performed in 1911. The earliest version of the ballet with designs by Gontcharova, was presented by* Opéra et Ballet Privés de Paris *at the* Théâtre des Champs Elysées *in 1926. One with designs by Mstislav Doboujinsky was performed in New York in 1942: another with designs by Gontcharova appeared in Paris in 1940, and it is for this last that the scene in Plate 173 and the costume designs in Plates 171 and 172 were made.*

# Short Bibliography

ALEXANDRE, Arsène and Jean COCTEAU. *The Decorative Art of Léon Bakst*, London, 1913.

AMBERG, George. *Art in Modern Ballet*, New York, 1946.

BEAUMONT, Cyril W. *Complete Book of Ballets*, London, 1937.

BEAUMONT, Cyril W., and Sacheverell SITWELL. *The Romantic Ballet in Lithographs of the Time*, London, 1938.

BEAUMONT, Cyril W. *Five Centuries of Ballet Design*, London, 1939.

BEAUMONT, Cyril W. *Ballet Design Past and Present*, London, 1946.

BENOIS, Alexandre. *Reminiscences of the Russian Ballet*, London, 1941.

BJURSTRÖM, Per. *Giacomo Torelli and Baroque Stage Design*, Stockholm, 1961.

BLASIS, Carlo. *Traité de l'Art de la Danse*, Milan, 1820.

BUCKLE, Richard. *Catalogue of the Diaghilev Exhibition from the Edinburgh Festival*, London, 1954.

COCTEAU, Jean and Arsène ALEXANDRE. *The Decorative Art of Léon Bakst*, London, 1913.

COGNIAT, Raymond. *Décors de Théâtre*, Paris, 1930.

DECURGIS, Nicole and Suzanne REYMOND. *Le Décor de Théâtre en France*, Paris, 1954.

DUNCAN, Isidora (ed. by Shelton Cheney). *The Art of the Dance*, New York, 1928.

ENCICLOPEDIA DELLO SPETTACOLO, Rome, 1954.

FISCHER, Carlos. *Les Costumes de l'Opéra*, Paris, 1931.

FÜLÖP-MILLER, René and Joseph GREGOR. *Das Russische Theater*, Zürich, 1927.

GADAN-PAMARD, Francis and R. MAILLARD (ed.). *Dictionaire du Ballet Moderne*, Paris, 1957. (English translation, London, 1959.)

GATTI, Carlo. *Il Teatro alla Scala (1778-1963)*, Milan, 1964.

GONTCHAROVA, Natalie, M. LARIONOV and P. VORMS. *Les Ballets Russes. Serge de Diaghilev et la Decoration Théâtrale*, Belvès, 1955.

GREGOR, Joseph and René FÜLÖP-MILLER. *Das Russische Theater*, Zürich, 1927.

GREGOR, Joseph. *Kulturgeschichte des Ballets*, Vienna, 1944.

GRIGORIEV, Serge L. *The Diaghilev Ballet*, London, 1953.

GUEST, Ivor. *The Romantic Ballet in England*, London, 1954.

GUEST, Ivor. *The Ballet of the Second Empire* (2 vols.), London, 1953–1955.

HASKELL, Arnold. *Diaghilev*, London, 1935.

HASKELL, Arnold. *Ballet*, London, 1938.

HASKELL, Arnold. *Ballet Panorama*, London, 1938.

KIRSTEIN, Lincoln and Muriel STUART. *The Classic Ballet. Basic Technique and Terminology*, London, 1953.

LACROIX, Paul (ed.). *Ballets et Mascarades de Cour de Henri III à Louis XIV Recueillis et Publiés, d'après les Editions Originales etc.*, Geneva, 1868–70.

LARIONOV, M. (*see* GONTCHAROVA).

LAVER, James. *Drama; its Costume and Décor*, London, 1951.

LE BEAU, Madame Pierre Adrien. *Gallerie des Modes et Costumes Français*, Paris, 1778 (réimpression, 1911–1914).

LIFAR, Serge. *Ballet Traditional to Modern*, London, 1954.

LIFAR, Serge. *A History of Russian Ballet*, London, 1954.

MAILLARD, Robert and F. GADAN-PAMARD (ed.). *Dictionaire du Ballet Moderne*, Paris, 1957. (English translation, London, 1959).

MAYOR, Hyatt and Janos SCHOLZ. *Baroque and Romantic Stage Design*, New York, 1950.

MENESTRIER, Claude François. *Des Ballets Anciens et Modernes, selon les Regles du Théâtre*, Paris, 1682.

MENESTRIER, Claude François. *Traité des Tournois, Joustes, Carrousels etc.*, Lyons, 1669.

NOVERRE, Jean Georges (trs. C. W. Beaumont). *Letters on Dancing and Ballets (1803)*, London, 1930.

PARNACK, Valentin. *Gontcharova: Larionov*, Paris, 1919.

PROPERT, Walter Archibald. *The Russian Ballet in Western Europe 1909–20*, London, 1921.

PROPERT, Walter Archibald. *The Russian Ballet 1921–29*, London, 1931.

PRUNIÈRES, Henry. *Le Ballet de Cour en France avant Benserade et Lully*, Paris, 1914.

SCHOLZ, Janos and Hyatt MAYOR. *Baroque and Romantic Stage Design*, New York, 1950.

SITWELL, Sacheverell and C. W. BEAUMONT. *The Romantic Ballet in Lithographs of the Time*, London, 1938.

SMITH, William C. *The Italian Opera and Contemporary Ballet in London, 1789–1820*, London (Society for Theatre Research), 1955.

STUART, Muriel and Lincoln KIRSTEIN. *The Classic Ballet. Basic Technique and Terminology*, London, 1953.

SVÉTLOV, Valérian. *Le Ballet Contemporain*, St. Petersburg-Paris, 1912.

VORMS, P. (*see* GONTCHAROVA).

WEIGERT, Roger Armand. *Jean I Berain*, Paris, 1937.

Wt. 3627   K24

S.O. Code No. 29–1668*

# THE PLATES

1. JACQUES PATIN. *Le Ballet Comique de la Reine*, 1581. Etching, 1582.

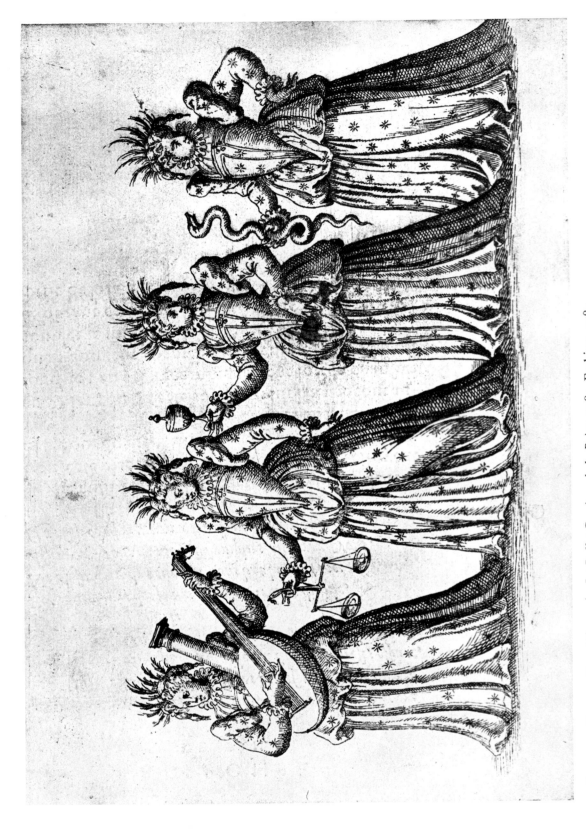

2. JACQUES PATIN. *Four Virtues in* Le Ballet Comique de la Reine, 1581. Etching, 1582.

3. BERNARDO BUONTALENTI. Design for scenery of *Intermezzo II*, Florence, 1589. Drawing.

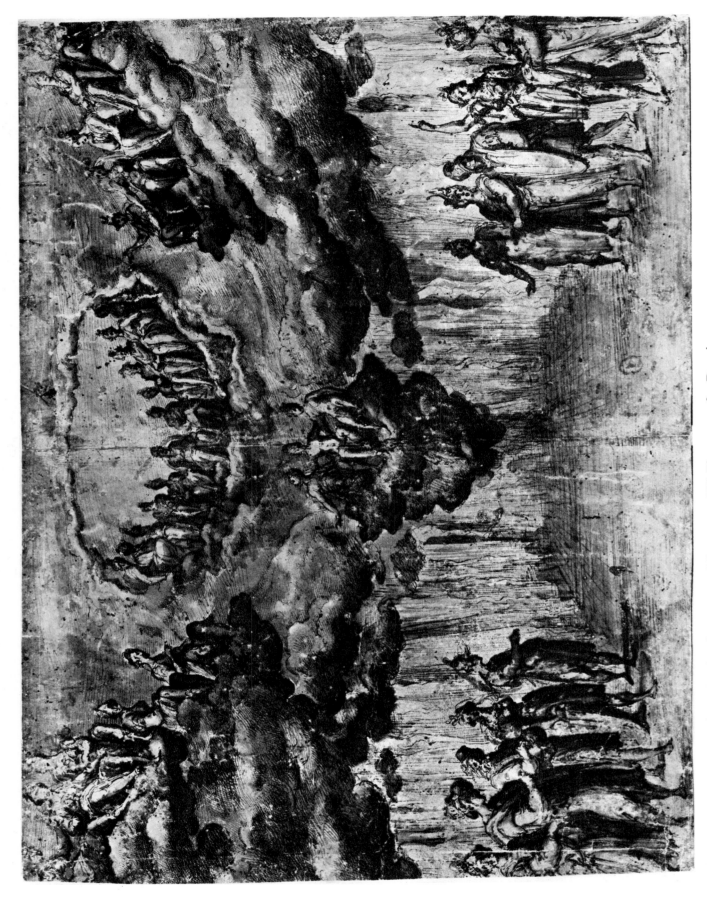

4. BERNARDO BUONTALENTI. Design for scenery of *Intermezzo VI*, Florence, 1589. Drawing.

5. BERNARDO BUONTALENTI. Design for costumes, probably in the Florentine *Intermezzi* of 1589. Coloured drawing.

V.A.M

6. AGOSTINO CARACCI, after Buontalenti. *Intermezzo III*, Florence, 1589. Engraving.

PALAZZO DELLA FAMA INTERMEDIO PRIMO

Remigio Canta Gallina F.

Conc: expers: nelle nobile del Ser:mo Prencipe d.
Toscana l'Ann: 1608. Giulio Parigi I:

7. REMIGIO CANTAGALLINA, after G. Parigi. First of six intermezzi, Florence, 1608. Etching.

8. Anonymous. Design for the costume of Hercules, *c.* 1600–1620. Coloured drawing.

9. Anonymous. Design for the costume of a prince, *c*. 1600–1620. Coloured drawing.

10. Anonymous. Design for a ballet costume, *c*. 1600–1620. Coloured drawing.

11. Anonymous. Design for a dancer with castanets, *c*. 1600–1620. Coloured drawing.

12. Anonymous. Design for a ballet costume, *c.* 1600–1620. Coloured drawing.

13. Anonymous. Design for a ballet costume, *c.* 1600–1620. Coloured drawing.

14. Anonymous. Design for the costume of a satyr, *c.* 1600–1620. Coloured drawing.

PRIMO INTERMEDIO DELLA VEGLIA DELLA LIBERATIONE DI TIRRENO FATTA NELLA SALA DELLE COM
DIE DEL SER.<sup>mo</sup> GRAN DVCA DI TOSCANA IL CARNOVALE DEL 1616. DOVE SI RAP.<sup>ta</sup> IL MONTE D'ISCHIA CON IL GIGANTE
TIFEO SOTTO.

15. JACQUES CALLOT, after G. Parigi. *Intermezzo I* in *La Liberazione di Tirreno e d'Arnea*, 1617.
Etching.

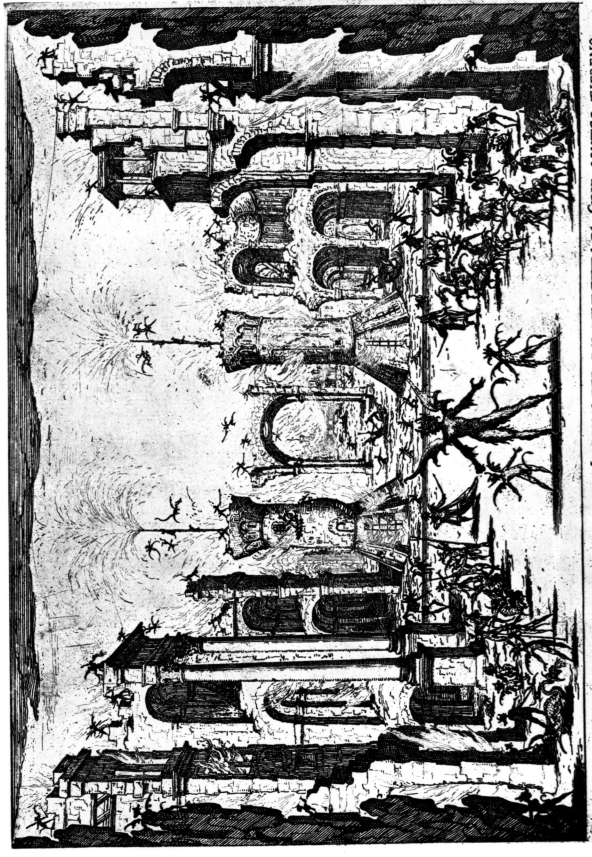

16. JACQUES CALLOT, after G. Parigi. *Intermezzo II* in *La Liberazione di Tirreno e d'Arnea*, 1617. Etching.

TERZO INTERMEDIO DOVE SI VIDÈ VENIRE AMORE CON TVTTA LA SVA CORTE A DIVIDER LA BATTAGLIA.

17. JACQUES CALLOT, after G. Parigi. *Intermezzo III in La Liberazione di Tirreno e d'Arnea*, 1617. Etching.

18. ALFONSO PARIGI. Design for scenery in *Le Nozze degli Dei*, 1634. Drawing.

STEFANO DELLA BELLA, after A. Parigi. Scene III in *Le Nozze degli Dei*, 1634. Etching 1637.

QVARTA SCENA DI MARE

20. STEFANO DELLA BELLA, after A. Parigi. Scene IV in *Le Nozze degli Dei*, 1634. Etching, 1637.

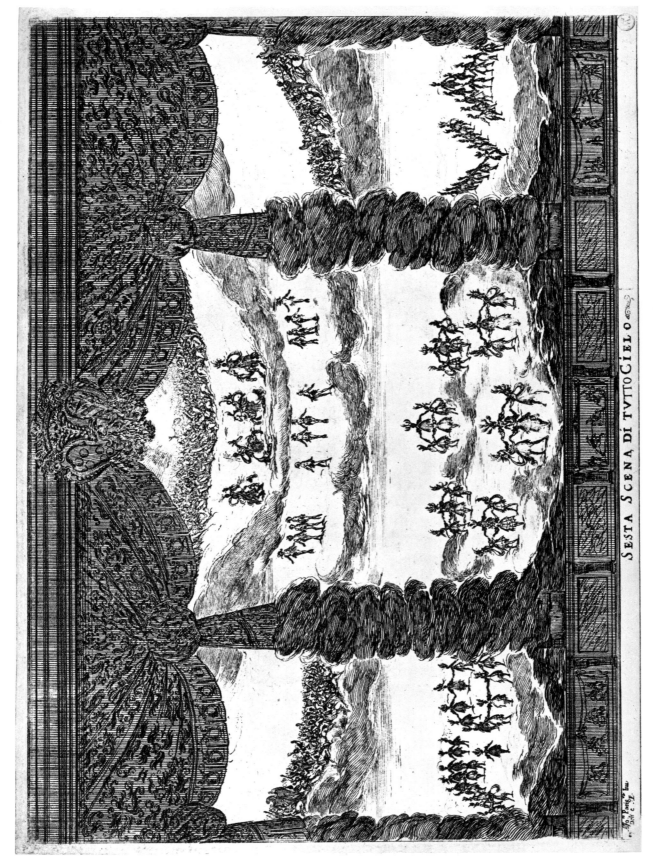

SESTA SCENA DI TVTTO CIELO

21. STEFANO DELLA BELLA, after A. Parigi. Scene VI in *Le Nozze degli Dei*, 1634. Etching, 1637.

22. Anonymous. Design for the costume of an Amazon, *c.* 1650. Coloured drawing.

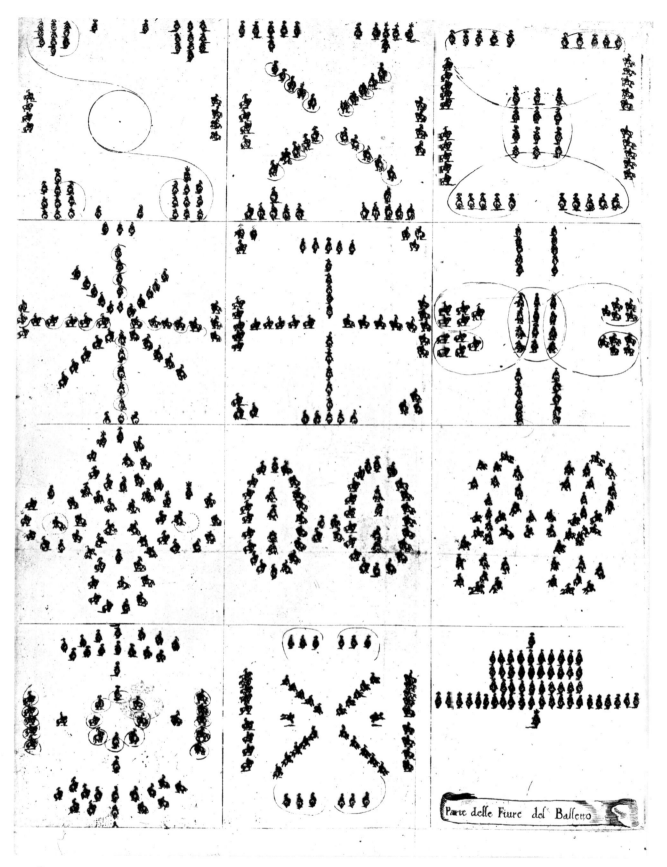

23. STEFANO DELLA BELLA. Plans for an equestrian ballet, 1652. Etching.

24. HENRY GISSEY (attributed to). Design for a dancer in a *ballet de cour*, *c*. 1660–1673. Drawing.

25. HENRY GISSEY (attributed to). Design for a dancer in a *ballet de cour*, *c.* 1660–1673. Drawing.

26. HENRY GISSEY (attributed to). Design for a dancer in a *ballet de cour*, *c.* 1660–1673. Drawing.

27. HENRY GISSEY (attributed to). Design for a bird costume in a *ballet de cour*, *c.* 1660–1673. Drawing.

28. HENRY GISSEY (attributed to). Design for the costume of an apothecary in a *ballet de cour*, *c.* 1660. Coloured drawing.

29. HENRY GISSEY (attributed to). Design for a dancer in a *ballet de cour*, *c.* 1660.
Coloured drawing.

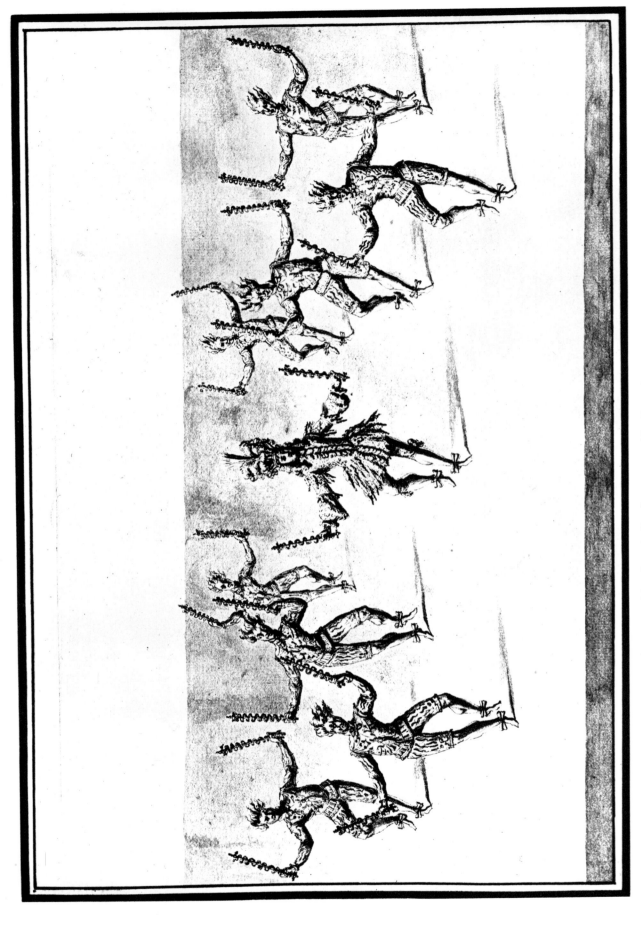

30. Anonymous. Design for a choreographic composition in a *ballet de cour*, *c.* 1660. Drawing.

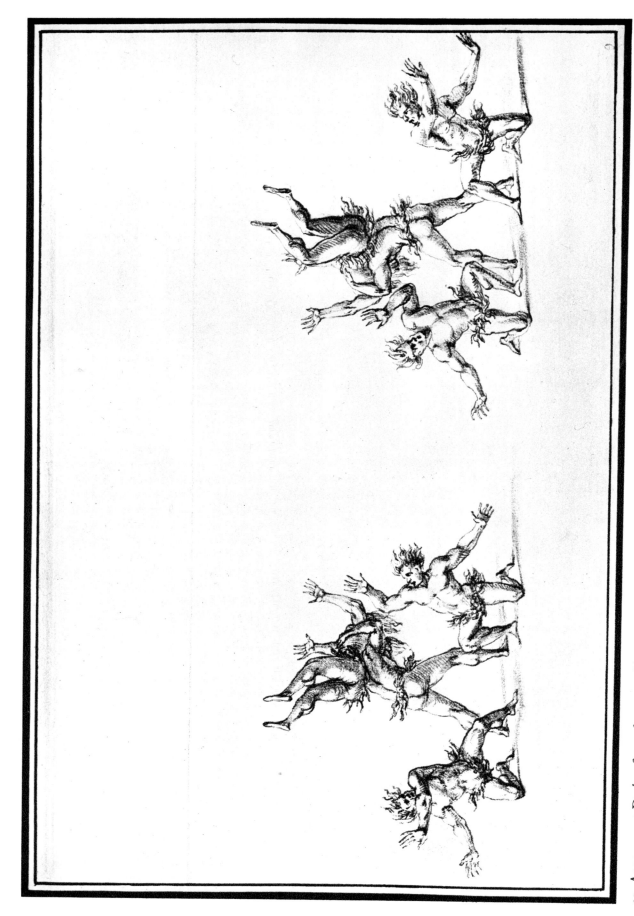

31. Anonymous. Design for a choreographic composition in a *ballet de cour, c.* 1660. Drawing.

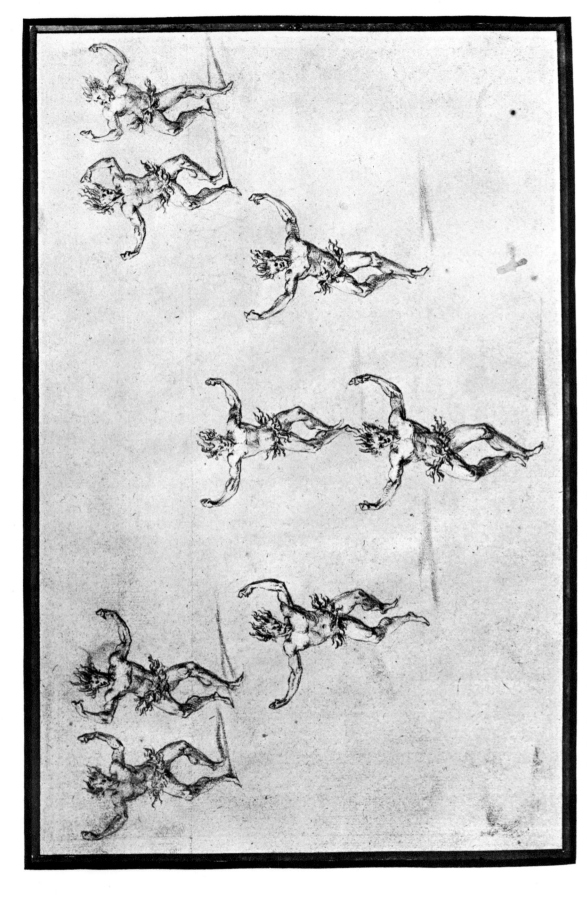

32. Anonymous. Design for a choreographic composition in a *ballet de cour*, *c.* 1660. Drawing.

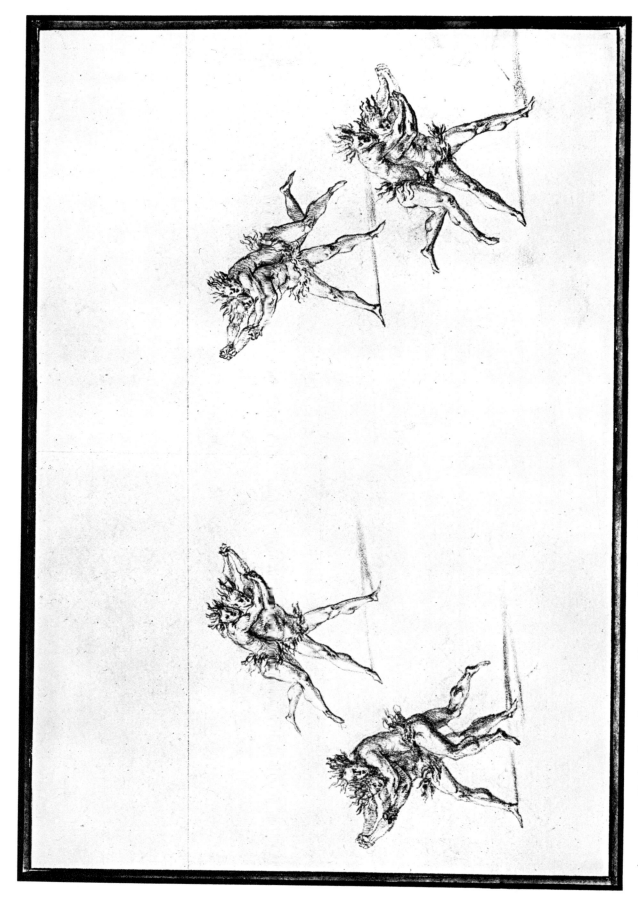

33. Anonymous. Design for a choreographic composition in a *ballet de cour*, *c.* 1660. Drawing.

34. Anonymous. Design for a choreographic composition in a *ballet de cour*, *c.* 1660. Drawing.

35. HENRY GISSEY (attributed to). Design for the costume of a lictor
in the Carrousel of 1662. Coloured drawing.

36. FRANÇOIS CHAUVEAU, after H. Gissey. Philippe duc d'Orléans in the Carrousel of 1662. Engraving.

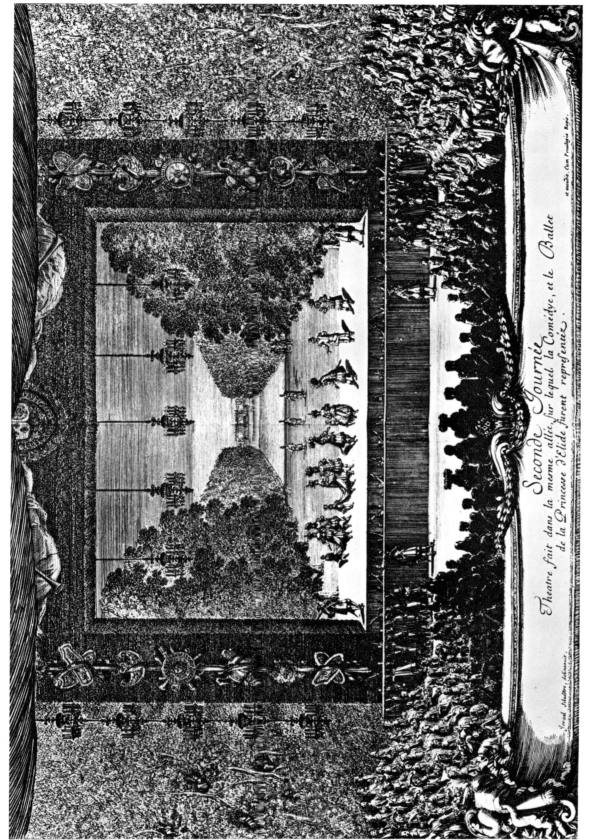

37. ISRAEL SILVESTRE. The performance of *La Princesse d'Élide*, 1664. Etching, 1673–1674.

38. ISRAEL SILVESTRE. The Island of Alcine in *Le Palais d'Alcine*, 1664. Etching, 1673–1674.

*Ballet des quatre Géants et quatre Nains.*

39. JOHANNES WORM (attributed to). *Ballet des Quatre Géants et Quatre Nains*, second half of 17th century. Engraving.

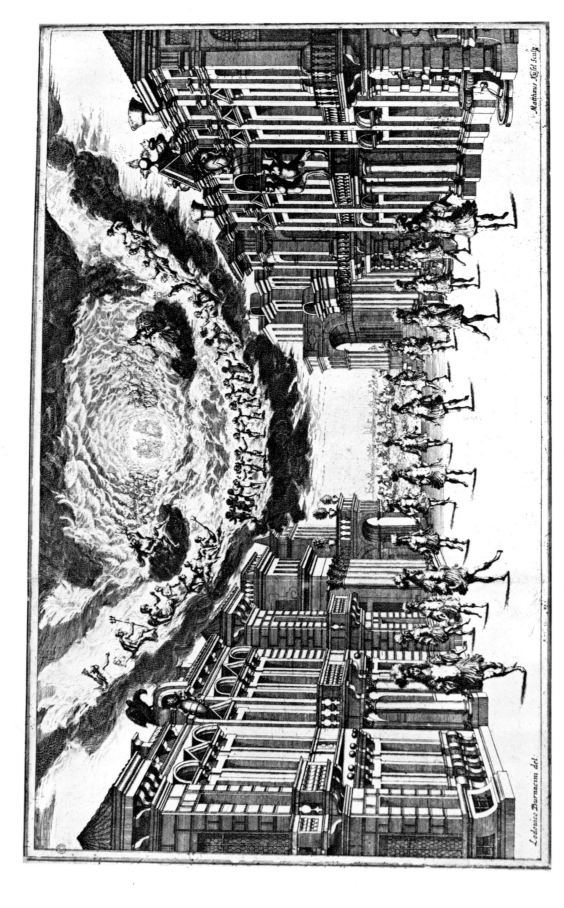

40. Matthaus Küsel, after L. O. Burnacini. The ballet in *Il Pomo d'Oro*, 1668. Engraving.

41. JEAN LOUIS BERAIN (Studio of). Design for the costume of a dancer, *c.* 1681. Coloured drawing.

J. Berin del.

42. JEAN DOLIVAR, after J. L. Berain. A nymph in *Le Triomphe de l'Amour*, 1681. Engraving.

43. JEAN DOLIVAR, after J. L. Berain. An Indian in *Le Triomphe de l'Amour*, 1681. Engraving.

44. JEAN LOUIS BERAIN (Studio of). Design for the costume of a female dancer, *c.* 1685. Drawing.

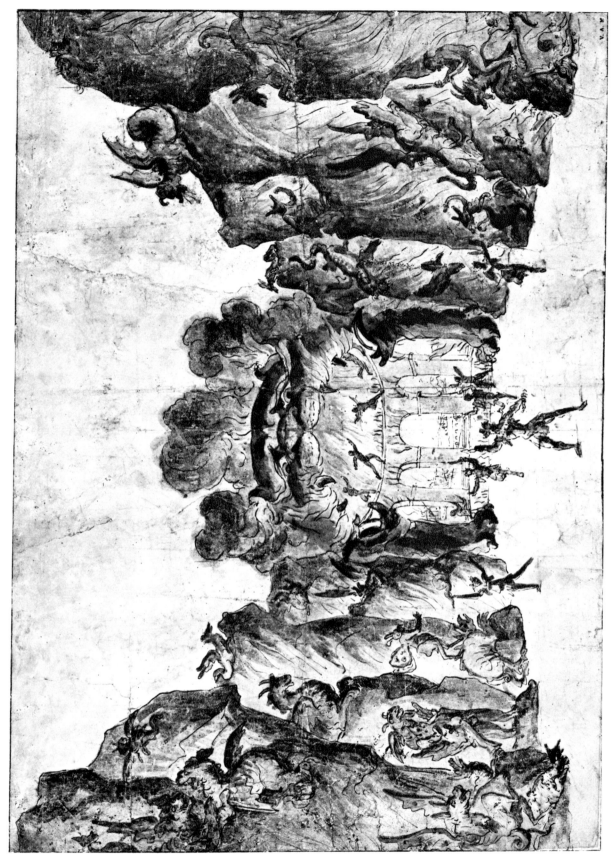

45. JEAN LOUIS BERAIN (attributed to). Design for an inferno scene, late 17th century. Coloured drawing.

Peint par R. Tournière.                    Gravé par F. Chereau

*LOUIS PÉCOUR*

*Pensionnaire du Roy, Compositeur des Balets de l'Académie Royalle*
*de Musique, et Maître a Danser de Madᵉ la Duchesse de Bourgogne.*

46. FRANÇOIS CHEREAU, after R. Levrac-Tournières. G. L. Pécourt, dancer and choreographer, *c.* 1710. Engraving.

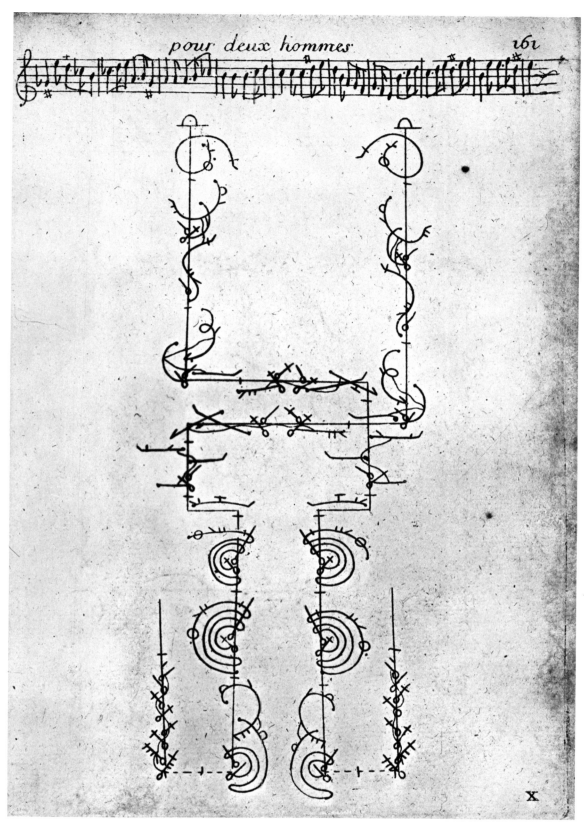

47. Anonymous. Canary for two male dancers in *Dido*. Etching, 1704.

48. PIETRO GIOVANNI ABBATI, after Ferdinando Galli. Design for a stage set. Etching, *c.* 1707.

49. Johann Georg Puschner. *Bourée*. Engraving, 1716.

50. JOHANN GEORG PUSCHNER. *Corrente.* Engraving, 1716.

51. JOHANN GEORG PUSCHNER. *Scaramuza*. Engraving, 1716.

52. JOHANN GEORG PUSCHNER. *Deta.* Engraving, 1716.

53. JOHANN GEORG PUSCHNER. *Narcisin*. Engraving, 1716.

54. JOHANN GEORG PUSCHNER. *Galiardo*. Engraving, 1716.

55. Johann Georg Puschner. *Zurlo bacho*. Engraving, 1716.

56. JOHANN ANDREAS PFEFFEL (the Elder), after Giuseppi Galli. Design for a stage set, *c.* 1720. Engraving, 1740.

57. P. LIOR (attributed to). Design for the costume of a fawn, *c.* 1744. Coloured drawing.

58. P. LIOR (attributed to). Design for the costume of a trumpeter, *c.* 1744. Coloured drawing.

59. CHARLES NICOLAS COCHIN (the Younger). The performance of *La Princesse de Navarre*, 1745.
Engraving.

60. Anonymous. Designs for dancers in a comedy-ballet, c. 1745. Coloured drawing.

Marvie delineavit

Horeolly Sculpsit

**BALET DU PRINCE DE SALERNE**
Exécuté a Fontainebleau en Novembre 1746.

24413 / 2

Ces deux danseurs, presqu'en naissant       Et dans l'âge ou l'on sent a peine,
Par leur dance ingenüe embelissent la scéne ;       Ils expriment tout ce qu'on sent

61. HORÉOLLY, after M. Marvie. *Le Ballet du Prince de Salerne*, 1746. Engraving.

62. LOUIS BOQUET. Design for the costume of a princess, *c.* 1750. Coloured drawing.

63. SANTE MANELLI, after Giovanni Galli. Illustration of scenery in *La Clemenza di Tito*, 1755. Engraving.

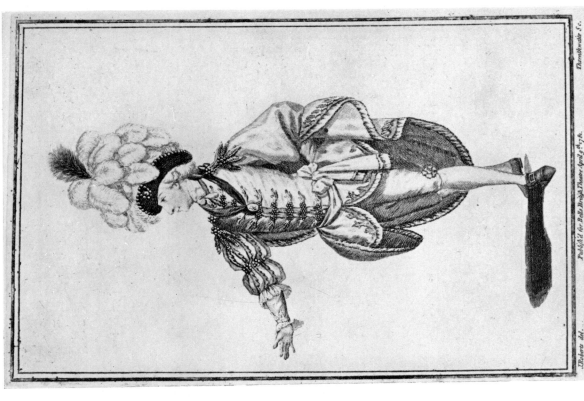

65. J. THORNTHWAITE, after J. Roberts. Gaëtan Vestris in
*Ninette à la Cour*, 1781. Engraving.

64. J. THORNTHWAITE, after J. Roberts. Signora Baccelli in *Les Amans
Surpris*, 1781. Engraving.

66. FRANCESCO BARTOLOZZI AND PASTORINI, after N. Dance. Auguste Vestris, 1781. Etching and engraving.

JASON ET MEDEE        BALLET TRAGIQUE.

67. FRANCESCO BARTOLOZZI, possibly after N. Dance. Gaëtan Vestris in *Jason and Medea*, 1781. Etching and aquatint.

68. PAUL SANDBY (attributed to). Two dancers, probably Gaëtan and Auguste Vestris, c. 1780–1781. Coloured drawing.

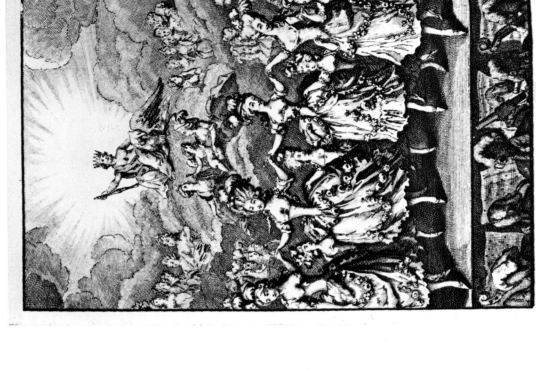

70. LOUIS BERTHET, after L. Binet. Ballet scene in *Psyché*, *c.* 1785. Engraving.

69. LOUIS BERTHET, after L. Binet. Ballet scene in *Armide et Renaud*, *c.* 1785. Engraving.

71. JEAN CONDÉ, after H. de Janvry. Mademoiselle Hilligsberg in *Le Jaloux Puni*, 1794. Stipple engraving.

72. TOMMASO PIROLI, after F. Rehberg. The sixth Attitude from *Lady Hamilton's Attitudes*, 1794. Engraving, 1797.

73. Anonymous, after A. L. Hirt. Theseus and Antiope in *Dädalus und Seine Statuen*, 1802. Coloured etching.

74. Anonymous, after A. L. Hirt. Cephalus and Aurora in *Dädalus und Seine Statuen*, 1802. Coloured etching.

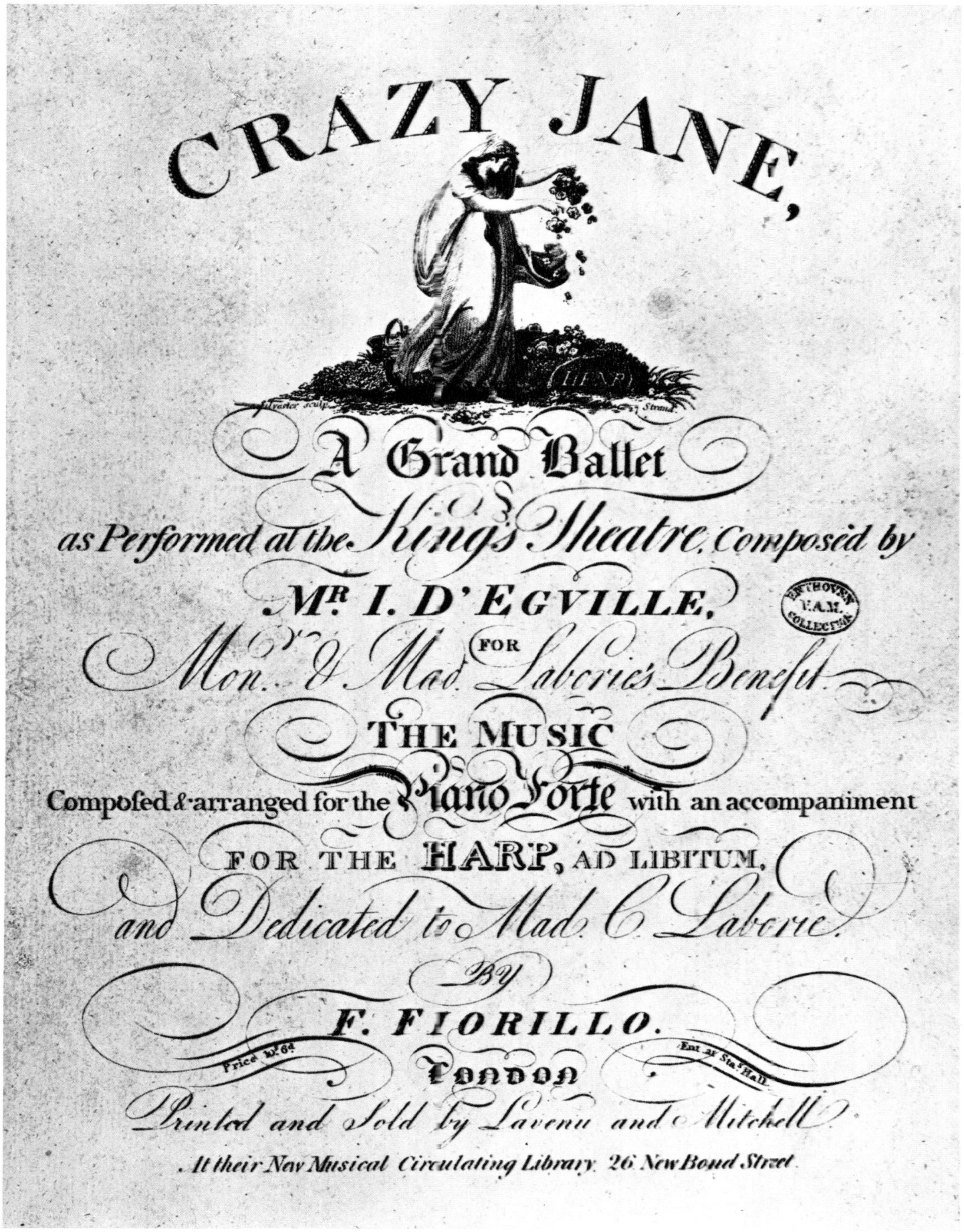

CRAZY JANE,

A Grand Ballet

as Performed at the King's Theatre, Composed by

MR I. D'EGVILLE,

FOR Mon. & Mad. Laborie's Benefit.

THE MUSIC

Composed & arranged for the Piano Forte with an accompaniment

FOR THE HARP, AD LIBITUM,

and Dedicated to Mad. C Laborie.

By

F. FIORILLO.

London

Printed and Sold by Lavenu and Mitchell

At their New Musical Circulating Library, 26 New Bond Street.

75. Anonymous. Title of the score for the music of *Crazy Jane*, 1805. Engraving.

*Joly, del.*                    *à Paris chez Martinet, Lib. rue du Coq, N.º 15.*

76. ADRIEN JOLY. Beaupré in *Paul et Virginie*, *c.* 1806. Coloured etching, 1820.

O Chute épouvantable et digne de mémoire!

77. PIERRE BAQUOY, after S. D. Mirys. Frontispiece of *La Danse, ou la Guerre des Dieux de l'Opéra*, 1808. Engraving.

78. Angelo Biasioli, after A. Sanquirico. Scene in *I Strelitzi*, 1811. Coloured etching and aquatint, *c.* 1827.

79. CAROLINA LOSE, after A. Sanquirico. Scene in *L'Alunno della Giumenta ossia l'Ippotoo Vendicato*, 1812. Coloured etching and aquatint, *c.* 1827.

80. CASARTELLI. Illustration of three kinds of ballet from *Traité . . . de l'Art de la Danse* by C. Blasis, 1820. Etching.

PADIGLIONE

*Ballo: La presa di Babilonia*                    *Milano presso l'incisore Stucchi*

81. STUCCHI AND D. LANDINI, after A. Sanquirico. Scene in *La Presa di Babilonia*, 1821. Etching and aquatint, *c.* 1823.

SALA CHE METTE AL GIARDINO.
*Ballé . Alfredo il Grande.*

82. STUCCHI AND D. LANDINI, after A. Sanquirico. Scene in *Alfredo il Grande*, 1822. Etching and aquatint, *c.* 1823.

*Pierson, dans Suzanne, Ballet de Mᵣ Blache.*

Th. de la Porte Sᵗ Martin.

Boullay Sc.　　　Acte Iᵉ.　Scène Iʳᵉ.　　　Ch.

A Paris chez Maranel Rue du Coq Nᵒ 15.

83. BOULLAY, after C. Charles. Pierson in *Suzanne*, *c.* 1820. Coloured etching, 1820.

84. C. CHARLES. Pierson and Madame Pierson in *La Fille Soldat*, *c*. 1820. Coloured etching.

Lith de Engelmann.

LE DUC MEVILLA. (Mᴿ. Albert.)

Dans Clary Ballet en 3 Actes. (Acadⁱ. Rᵉ. de musique.)

85. Anonymous, after A. S. Garnerey. Monsieur Albert in *Clari*, *c*. 1820. Coloured lithograph.

*Lith. de G. Engelmann.*

GERMANO *Valet du Duc.* (M. Ferdinand.)

*Dans Clary, Ballet, pantomime en 3 actes. (Académie R. de Musique.)*

86. Anonymous, after A. S. Garnerey. Monsieur Ferdinand in *Clari, c.* 1820.
Coloured lithograph.

Une DAME Amie du Duc. (Mᵐᵉ Elie)
*Dans Clary*, Ballet, pantomime en 3 actes. (Académie Rˡᵉ de Musique.)

Lith de G. Engelmann

87. Anonymous, after A. S. Garnerey. Madame Élie in *Clari, c.* 1820. Coloured lithograph.

8.

Une jeune COMÉDIENNE. (M^lle Brocard)
Dans Clary, Ballet, pantomime en 3 actes. (Académie R.le de Musique)

Lith. de G. Engelmann.

88. Anonymous, after A. S. Garnerey. Mademoiselle Brocard in *Clari*, *c*. 1820.
Coloured lithograph.

89. Anonymous, after A. S. Garnerey. A young Ephesian in *Olimpie*, *c*. 1820. Coloured lithograph.

90. Anonymous, after A. S. Garnerey. Milon in *Les Pages du duc de Vendôme*, *c.* 1820.
Coloured lithograph.

91. FAUCONNIER, after H. Lecomte. Young Gaulish woman in *Pharamond*, *c.* 1820.
Coloured lithograph.

92. FAUCONNIER, after H. Lecomte. Frankish warrior in *Pharamond*, c. 1820.
Coloured lithograph.

*Vornehme tanzende Bucharen.*

93. HEINRICH STÜRMER, after W. Hensel. Bucharian dancers in *Lalla Rûkh*, 1821. Coloured etching, 1822.

*Stürmer fecit.*

*Vornehme tanzende Indier.*

94. Hienrich Stürmer, after W. Hensel. Indian dancers in *Lalla Rûkh*, 1821. Coloured etching, 1822.

Waldeck del:

Printed by Rawer & Forster.

**MONS<sup>R</sup>. ALBERT.**

From the Academy of Music, Paris.    In the Character of *Alcides*.    King's Theatre.

Published by H Berthoud. London. 1821.

95. F. WALDECK. Monsieur Albert in *Alcide*, 1821. Lithograph.

96. L. CASTELLINI, after A. Sanquirico. Scene in *Cleopatra in Tarso*, 1821. Coloured etching and aquatint *c.* 1827.

97. L. CASTELLINI, after A. Sanquirico. Scene in *Maometto*, 1822. Coloured etching and aquatint, *c.* 1827.

98. ROBERT COOPER, after F. Waldeck. Monsieur Le Blond at the King's Theatre, 1822.
Coloured stipple engraving.

99. Anonymous. Mademoiselle Bigotini and Ferdinand Albert in *Cendrillon*, 1823.
Coloured etching and engraving.

100. CAROLINA LOSE, after A. Sanquirico. Scene in *Il Naufragio di La Peyrouse*, 1825. Coloured etching and aquatint, *c.* 1827.

101. CAROLINA LOSE, after A. Sanquirico. Scene in *Elerz e Zulmida*, 1826. Coloured etching and aquatint, *c*. 1827.

102. ALFRED EDWARD CHALON. Mademoiselle Brocard and Mélanie Duval in *La Naissance de Vénus*, 1826. Coloured drawing.

Goslin
Carnaval de Venise
ou tout ce que vous voudrez.
1830.

Il est, il est, il est toujours le même.

103. ALFRED EDWARD CHALON. Louis François Gosselin in
*Le Carnaval de Venise, c.* 1830. Water-colour.

104. ALFRED EDWARD CHALON. Zoé Beaupré in *Kenilworth*, *c.* 1831. Water-colour.

LA BAYADÈRE.

105. ALFRED EDWARD CHALON. Marie Taglioni in *Le Dieu et la Bayadère*. Lithograph, 1831.

FLORE.

106. ALFRED EDWARD CHALON. Marie Taglioni in *Flore et Zéphire*.
Lithograph, 1831.

*Levasseur del.ᵗ*

SIG.ᵗ SAMENGO ᴀɴᴅ MAD. BRUGNOLI.
*In the Grand Ballad.*
L'ANNEAU MAGIQUE.

London Published by R. Ackermann, 96, Strand, May 1832.
Printed by Lefèvre Lemercier & Co 2 1 Lesc' Sq.

107. LEVASSEUR. Paolo Samengo and Amalia Brugnoli in *L'Anneau Magique*, 1832.
Coloured lithograph.

SIG.ᴿ SAMENGO ᴬᴺᴰ MAD.ᴱ BRUGNOLI,
*In the Grand Ballet*
L'ANNEAU MAGIQUE
*London Published by R. Ackermann 96 Strand May 1832*
Printed by Meifred Lemercier & Co 24 Leicester Sq.

108. LEVASSEUR. Paolo Samengo and Amalia Brugnoli in *L'Anneau Magique*, 1832.
Coloured lithograph.

Costume de Mᵐᵉ NOBLET. rôle D'EFFIE,
dans la Sylphide, Ballet.
Académie Royale de Musique.

Maleuvre S.

Chez Hautecœur Martinet, Libraire rue du Coq. N° 13 et 15, Paris.

109. P. MALEUVRE. Lise Noblet in *La Sylphide*, 1832.
Coloured etching.

110. ALFRED EDWARD CHALON. Marie Taglioni in *La Sylphide*, 1832. Coloured lithograph, *c.* 1846.

Portraits of Carlotta Grisi and M. Perrot.

A Scene in the Ballet, called 'Le Rossignol,' as performed at the King's Theatre.

Drawn and Etched by T. Jones; and Aquatinted by Hunt.
Published by Bell, Removed to Nr 28, Craven Street, Strand, London, June 1, 1836.

111. T. JONES AND GEORGE HUNT. A scene in *Le Rossignol*, 1836. Aquatint.

## COSTUME ESPAGNOL.

Porté par M.<sup>lle</sup> Fanny Essler dans le Diable boiteux.

112. JACQUES DEVÉRIA. Fanny Elssler in *Le Diable Boiteux*, c. 1836–1838.
Coloured lithograph, 1838.

113. Anonymous. Fanny Elssler in *The Gypsy*, 1839. Lithograph.

114. J. Bouvier. Marie Taglioni and A. Guerra in *L'Ombre*, 1840. Coloured lithograph, *c.* 1846.

V.A.M.

*Mad.lle Carlotta Grisi and Mons.r Perrot, La Esmeralda*

115. J. Bouvier. Carlotta Grisi and Jules Perrot in *La Esmeralda*, 1844. Coloured lithograph, *c.* 1846.

116. J. BOUVIER. Carlotta Grisi and Jules Perrot in *La Polka*, 1844. Coloured lithograph, *c.* 1846.

117. Anonymous. Scene in *Éoline, ou la Fille de la Dryade*, 1845. Wood engraving.

118. ALFRED EDWARD CHALON. Carlotta Grisi, Marie Taglioni, Lucile Grahn and Fanny Cerito in the *Pas de Quatre*, 1845. Coloured lithograph, *c.* 1846.

119. JOHN BRANDARD. Lucile Grahn in *Catarina, ou La Fille du Bandit*, 1846.
Coloured lithograph.

120. SMYTH, after Samuel Read. Scene in *Electra, ou la Pleiade Perdue*, 1849. Wood engraving.

121. LOUIS VEIT, after J. R. de Baux. Élise Casati in *The Adventures of Flick and Flock*.
Coloured lithograph, 1859.

122. LOUIS VEIT. Minna Kitzing and Anna Selling in *The Adventures of Flick and Flock*. Coloured lithograph, 1859.

123. LOUIS VEIT. Wilhelm Ebel in *Morgano*. Coloured Lithograph, 1859.

124. LOUIS VEIT. Nadejda Bogdanova in *La Esmeralda*, *c*. 1856–1859. Coloured lithograph, 1859.

V.A.M.

E.812—1932

125. CHARLES WILHELM (pseud.). Design for a costume in *The Black Crook*,
1881. Coloured drawing.

126. CHARLES WILHELM (pseud.). Design for
a costume in *Aladdin*, 1885. Coloured drawing.

127. CHARLES WILHELM (pseud.). Design for a costume
in a pantomime, 1885. Coloured drawing.

128. CHARLES WILHELM (pseud.). Design for costumes in *Rose d'Amour*, 1888.
Coloured drawing.

129. LUCIEN BESCHE. Design for a costume in a ballet-divertissement, 1890. Coloured drawing.

E.3326-1934

130. ATTILIO COMELLI. Design for a costume in a ballet-divertissement,
c. 1893. Water-colour.

131. ALEXANDER BENOIS. Design for the costume of Nijinsky in *Le Pavillon d'Armide*, 1907.
Coloured drawing.

132. Nicolai Roerich. Design for a camp in *Polovtsian Dances from Prince Igor*, 1909. Tempera and body-colour.

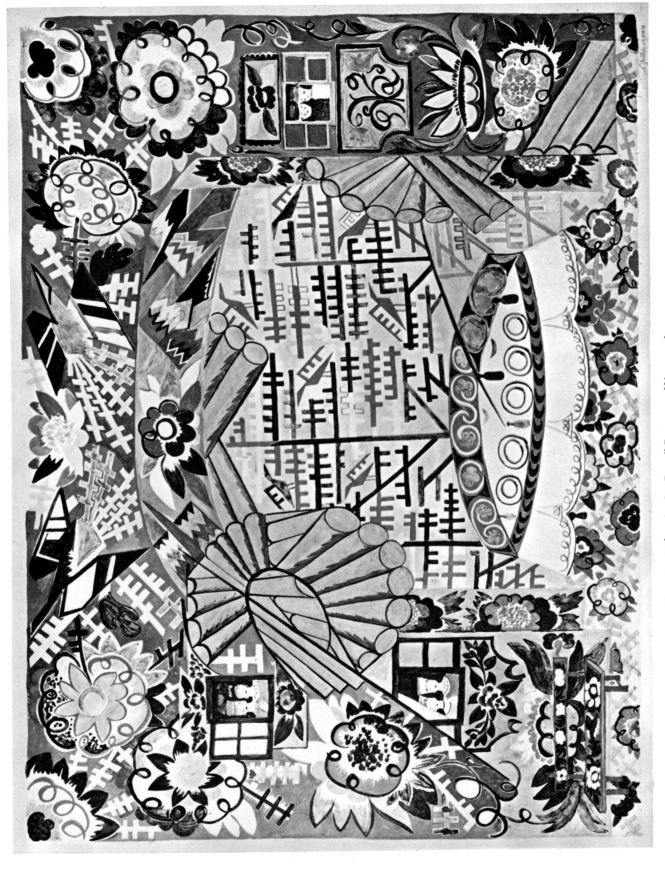

133. NATALIA GONTCHAROVA. Project for a backdrop in *Le Coq d'Or*, 1914. Water-colour.

134. Natalia Gontcharova. Design for a costume in *Le Coq d'Or*, 1914. Coloured drawing.

135. NATALIA GONTCHAROVA. Design for a costume in *Le Coq d'Or*, 1914. Coloured drawing.

136. NATALIA GONTCHAROVA. Design for a costume in *Le Coq d'Or*, 1914. Coloured drawing.

N Gontcharowa.

137. NATALIA GONTCHAROVA. Design for a costume in *Le Coq d'Or*, 1914. Coloured drawing.

138. ALBERT RUTHERSTON. Design for a costume in *The Awakening of Flora*, 1914. Coloured drawing.

139. ERNST STERN. Design for a scene in *Die Grüne Flöte*, 1916. Lithograph.

140. MIKHAIL LARIONOV. Design for a costume in *Le Soleil de Nuit*, 1915.
Coloured drawing.

141. NATALIA GONTCHAROVA. Design for a costume in *Sadko*, 1916. Coloured drawing.

142. MIKHAIL LARIONOV. Design for the costume of Kikimora in the ballet *Kikimora*, 1916. Coloured drawing.

143. MIKHAIL LARIONOV. Design for the costume of the Cat in *Kikimora*, 1916.
Coloured drawing.

144. MIKHAIL LARIONOV. Design for a costume in *Histoires Naturelles*, 1916. Coloured drawing.

145. MIKHAIL LARIONOV. Design for a drop-curtain in *Les Contes Russes*, 1917. Coloured drawing.

146. MIKHAIL LARIONOV. Design for a stage set in *Les Contes Russes*, 1917. Body-colour, 1916.

147. MIKHAIL LARIONOV. Gontcharova, Diaghilev, Massine and Beppo, c. 1917. Drawing.

148. PAUL NASH. Design for the stage setting in *The Truth about the Russian Dancers*, 1920. Coloured drawing.

Design for Costume for
Madame Karsavina.

149. PAUL NASH. Design for a costume in *The Truth about the Russian Dancers*, 1920.
Coloured drawing.

Costume
for
The Corps de Ballet
"The Truth about
the Russian
Dancers."

150. PAUL NASH. Design for a costume in *The Truth about the Russian Dancers*, 1920.
Coloured drawing.

151. MIKHAIL LARIONOV. Design for a costume in *Chout*, 1921.
Coloured drawing, 1915.

152. MIKHAIL LARIONOV. Design for a costume in *Chout*, 1921. Coloured drawing, 1915.

153. LÉON BAKST. Design for a costume in *The Sleeping Princess*, 1921. Coloured drawing.

154. LÉON BAKST. Design for a costume in *The Sleeping Princess*, 1921.
Coloured drawing.

155. Léon Bakst. Design for a costume in *The Sleeping Princess*, 1921. Coloured drawing.

156. LÉON BAKST. Design for a costume in *The Sleeping Princess*, 1921. Coloured drawing.

157. Mikhail Larionov. Design for a costume in *Renard*, 1922. Water-colour.

158. Natalia Gontcharova. Design for a scene in *Les Noces*, 1923. Coloured drawing.

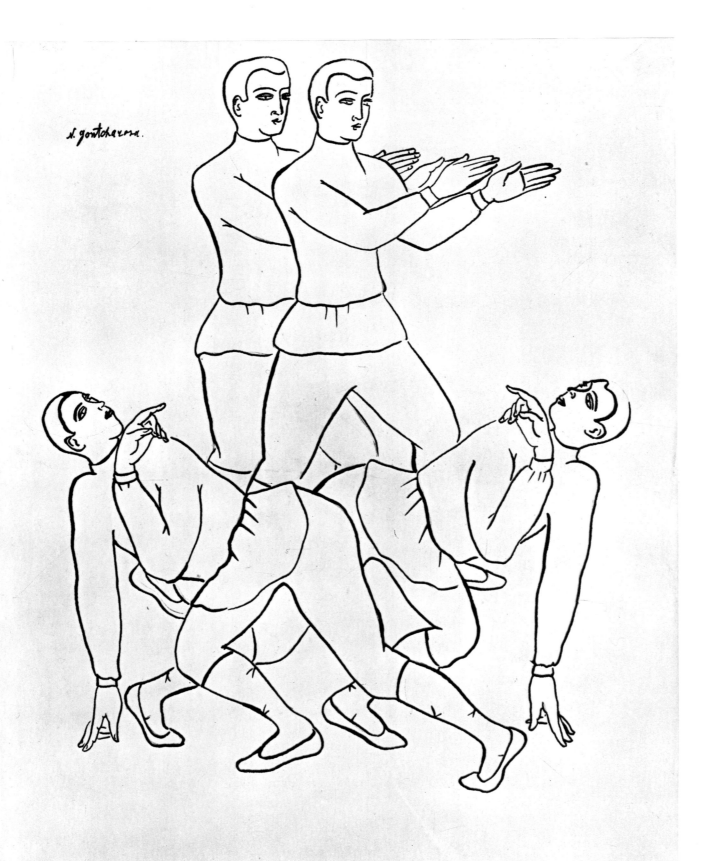

159. NATALIA GONTCHAROVA. Design for costumes and choreography in *Les Noces*, 1923. Drawing.

160. GEORGES BRAQUE. Design for a scene in *Les Fâcheux*, 1924. Coloured drawing.

161. GEORGES BRAQUE. Design for a costume in *Les Fâcheux*, 1924. Coloured drawing.

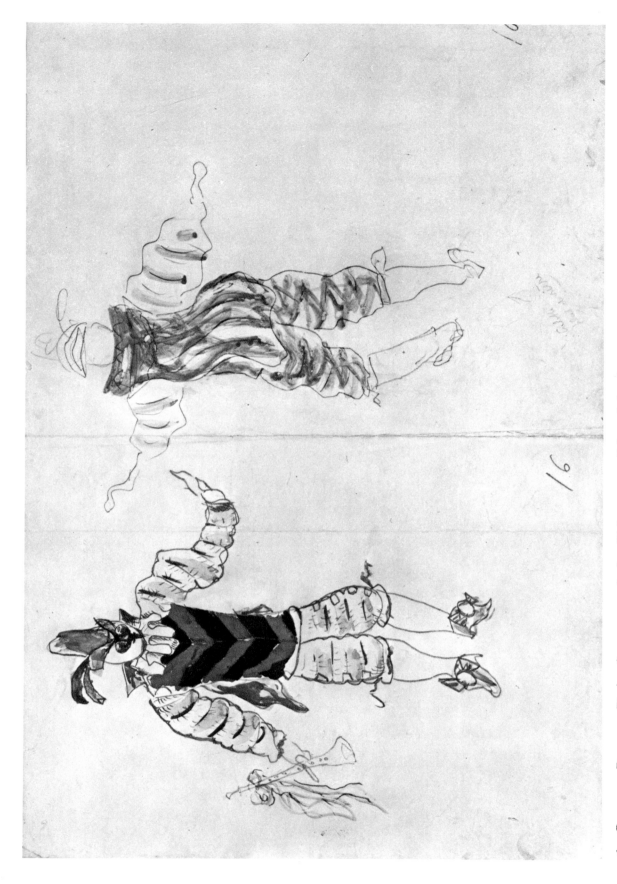

162. GEORGES BRAQUE. Design for a costume in *Les Fâcheux*, 1924. Coloured drawing.

163. VLADIMIR POLUNIN. Design for a drop-curtain for Diaghilev's Russian ballet, 1925. Water-colour.

164. NATALIA GONTCHAROVA. Design for a backcloth in *L'Oiseau de Feu*, 1926. Coloured drawing.

165. KONSTANTIN KOROVIN. Design for a costume in *La Gioconda*, 1927. Coloured drawing.

166. ALEXANDRA EXTER. Design for a stage setting in *Don Juan*, 1927. Body-colour.

167. ALEXANDRA EXTER. Design for a costume in *Don Juan*, 1927. Coloured drawing.

168. ALEXANDER BENOIS. Design for a scene in *Les Noces de L'Amour et Psyché*, 1928. Water-colour, 1927.

169. FERNAND LÉGER. Design for a stage set in a projected ballet, 1932. Water-colour.

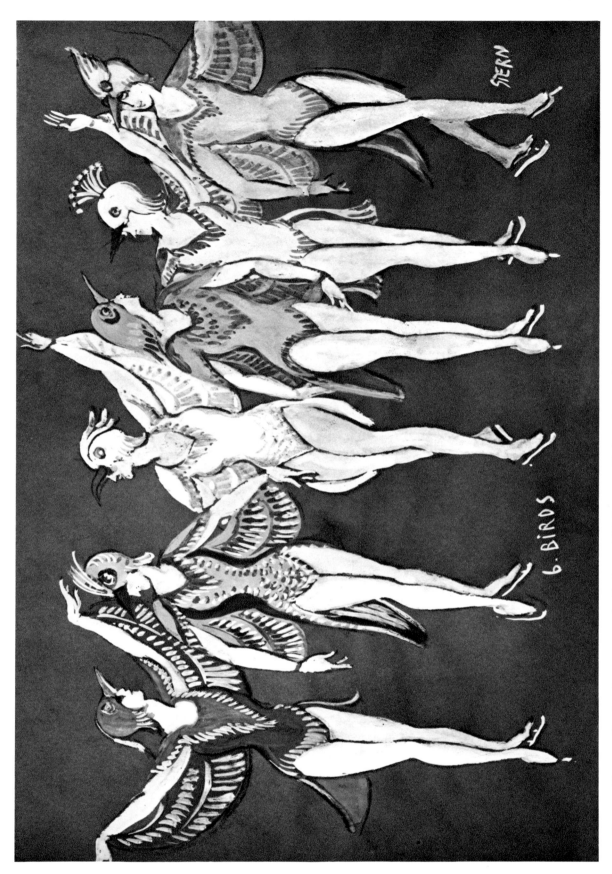

170. ERNST STERN. Design for costumes in *Enchanted Night*, 1937. Body-colour on blue paper.

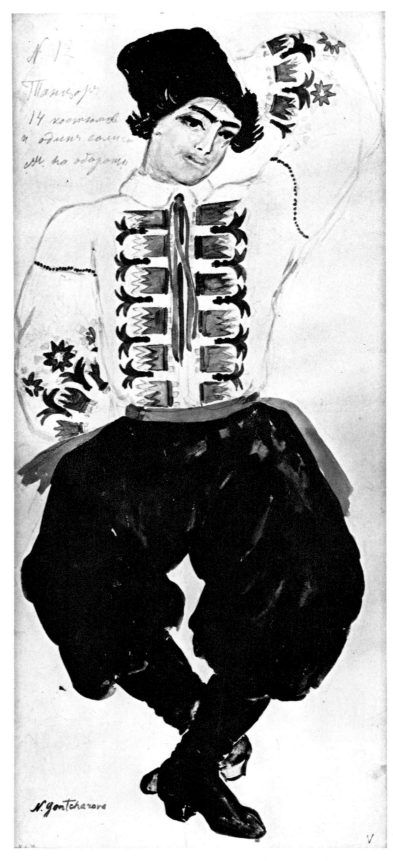

171. NATALIA GONTCHAROVA. Design for a costume in
*La Foire de Sorotchinsky*, 1940. Coloured drawing.

172. NATALIA GONTCHAROVA. Design for a costume in
*La Foire de Sorotchinsky*, 1940. Coloured drawing.

173. Natalia Gontcharova. Design for a stage setting for *La Foire de Sorotchinsky*, 1940. Water- and body-colour.